GREAT LAKE

Readers are encouraged to go to MissionPointPress.com to contact the author
or to find information on how to buy this book in bulk at a discounted rate.

MISSION POINT PRESS

Published by Mission Point Press
2554 Chandler Rd.
Traverse City, MI 49696
(231) 421-9513
MissionPointPress.com

Cover design by Kirsten Dalley Livingston
Illustrations by Heather Lee Shaw

ISBN: 978-1-958363-89-8
Library of Congress Control Number: 2023907789

Printed in the United States of America

GREAT LAKES

FACT

OR

FAKE?

DAVE DEMPSEY

ILLUSTRATIONS BY HEATHER LEE SHAW

MISSION POINT PRESS

CONTENTS

INTRODUCTION

The Great Lakes are impossible to overlook. Whether you're an astronaut circling the globe, a student examining a map of North America, or a tourist standing on the shore of one of the five lakes, they dominate our attention.

And yet, even most of those living within the roughly 200,000-square mile Great Lakes watershed[1] — an area larger than Thailand, Spain or Zimbabwe — don't know many of the most interesting things about them. Others who have never visited or studied them may lack knowledge or have misconceptions about the Great Lakes. Filling gaps and correcting misconceptions is a major purpose of this book.

But learning should stimulate minds and, might we suggest, even be fun. Gaining Great Lakes insights should be as inviting as deep-blue Lake Michigan on a sweltering summer day.

So, rather than lecturing, this book aims to challenge and entertain with 41 statements and asks you to guess what's fact or fake. No homework and no grading.

You are encouraged, however, to improve your Great Lakes knowledge, to become more intimate with the 20% of the world's available surface freshwater they contain.[2] You can then become a better steward of these majestic lakes, and an informed advocate for their protection.

GREAT LAKES
FACT OR FAKE?

TIDES

FACT OR FAKE?

The Great Lakes have tides.

Oceans have tides. Thanks to the gravitational pull of the sun and moon, oceans rise and fall twice each day.

Tides are long-period waves. They originate offshore and move toward coastlines. They are usually measured in feet, or meters.[3] At their extreme highs, tides in the Bay of Fundy, with shorelines touching Maine and the Canadian provinces of Nova Scotia and New Brunswick, average 47.6 feet (14.5 m) but have varied by as much as 53.5 feet (16.3 m) — the approximate height of a five-story building.[4]

So do the Great Lakes, with mammoth open waters, have tides?

It depends on your definition. The Great Lakes rise and fall in response to the gravitational pull of the sun and moon, but never more than 2 inches (about 5 cm). Consequently, the National Ocean Service considers the Great Lakes non-tidal.[5]

Still, much bigger water level changes occur over a short period of time in the Great Lakes. Known as seiches, the changes typically occur when high winds drive water from one side of a Great Lake to another. Seiches can even occur on Great Lakes' connecting waters like Lake St. Clair

between Michigan and Ontario. The effect is reminiscent of a sloshing bathtub, as water can surge back and forth several times. Waves related to seiches have reached 22 feet and washed people off piers and even resulted in fatalities on shores and piers. On June 26, 1954, a storm drove an eight-to-ten-foot swell from Chicago to the east shore of Lake Michigan. The water then rebounded, suddenly inundating a Chicago pier where anglers were fishing, sweeping many into the churning water. Eight people died.[6]

The Great Lakes also experience meteotsunamis. This phenomenon has led to waves 20 feet high.

The Great Lakes also experience meteotsunamis, large waves whipped up by changes in atmospheric pressure associated with storms. The phenomena has led to waves up to 20 feet high and multiple incidents along Lake Michigan's southern coast (10 killed in Grand Haven, Michigan, in 1929 and seven in 2003 in Michigan's Berrien County).

The Great Lakes have tides.

—barely

WHALES

FACT OR FAKE?

There are whales in the Great Lakes.

Each spring, visitors to Traverse City, Michigan, enter a
building inquiring about whales. Traverse City Tourism,
an agency that promotes recreational visits to the bays
and open waters of the Great Lakes, reports that visitors
walk in the doors "asking about the best places to view
migrating whales or wanting to know what companies offer
the best whale-watching tours."[7]

And the lore of the Great Lakes whale emerges again like a
humpback breaching the lake surface.

There is considerable evidence of whales in the Great
Lakes. One is the Great Lakes Whale Migration Station
on Beaver Island in northern Lake Michigan. The station
"collects migration data and records sighting of whales
as they migrate throughout the Great Lakes," the station
says on its Facebook page. A website, Lake Michigan Whale
Watching, informs visitors:

> As winter turns to spring and the cool waters of the lake
> are warmed by the sun, the freshwater sperm whales
> and dolphins begin their annual southbound 1,300-mile
> journey from Hudson Bay. Although there are a number of
> locks at Sault Ste. Marie, these beautiful and intelligent

*creatures forge a faster route through nearby streams,
and by mid-June, they have reached the breeding grounds
of southern Lake Michigan that they know as their
"summer home."*

The first whale watch cruise originating from Chicago took place in June 1985. The organizer pointed out that Great Lakes whales are rarely seen because, "Through evolution, the Great Lakes whales are carefully camouflaged."

Early in the 2000s, some Michigan instructors received a teaching aid, also distributed nationally to 1.2 million third through sixth grade students in the U.S., which described Great Lakes whales. The guide also mentioned the annual migration of the whales.

But whales thrive only in salt water, the nearest of which is 800 miles from Lake Michigan. Krill, the dietary staple of many whale species, do not live in freshwater. These small, shrimp-like crustaceans, averaging only about two inches, are critical to marine ecosystems.[8] Saltwater helps heal small wounds on whales. And the 1985 Chicago whale watching cruise was tongue-in-cheek.

Whale bones have been found in Michigan but may reflect their transport from ocean waters by Indigenous peoples through trade.

The point where Great Lakes water reaches saltwater in the Saint Lawrence River is home for about 900 beluga whales. White with a rounded forehead, female beluga whales

average 11.5 feet (3.5 m) while males can exceed 13 feet (4 m). The species faces threats from toxic chemicals that exit the Great Lakes system.[9] Flame retardants, mercury and pesticides all contribute to the toxic burden borne by the beluga.

So — whales may be close to the Great Lakes and influenced by the Great Lakes, but they do not live in the Great Lakes.

There are whales in the Great Lakes.

SIX GREAT LAKES

FACT OR FAKE?

There are six Great Lakes.

Traditionally, we have counted five Great Lakes. For decades, school children have been told they can use the acronym, HOMES, standing for the first letters in Huron, Ontario, Michigan, Erie and Superior, as a memory aid.

Some, however, argue there are at least six Great Lakes. One would be Lake St. Clair, at the center of the watershed between Huron and Erie. Without this lake and its connecting St. Clair and Detroit rivers, freighters would be unable to carry goods and commodities from the upstream Great Lakes to the downstream ones, and vice versa. Lake St. Clair and its connecting rivers are an essential element of the Great Lakes system.

But it is also a much smaller lake than any of the HOMES. The smallest of the five traditional Great Lakes, Erie, has a water volume of 116 cubic miles.[10] The volume of the largest, Superior, is 2,900 cubic miles.[11] The volume of Lake St. Clair, by contrast, is one to two cubic miles, depending on which information source is consulted.[12]

Despite its small surface area and water volume, Lake St. Clair — with Michigan and the United States on the north and west and Ontario and Canada on the south and east

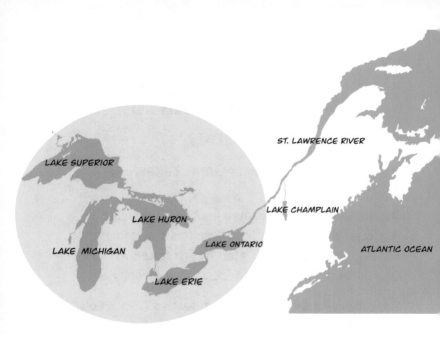

LAKE SUPERIOR

ST. LAWRENCE RIVER

LAKE HURON

LAKE CHAMPLAIN

LAKE MICHIGAN

LAKE ONTARIO

ATLANTIC OCEAN

LAKE ERIE

— is one of the most biologically productive spots in the Great Lakes system, luring sport anglers from both nearby and distant locations.

It could be argued that Ontario's Lake Nipigon is the sixth Great Lake. The largest lake entirely within Ontario, Nipigon is upstream of Lake Superior and the 28th largest lake in the world by surface area. Its volume is 59 cubic miles (248 cubic km).

Another contender for the title of the sixth Great Lake is Lake Champlain, which shares boundaries of New York State, Vermont, and Quebec. Lake Champlain flows northward, to the St. Lawrence River, which is also where water from the five traditional Great Lakes arrives. Its volume of more than six cubic miles is at a minimum three times more than Lake St. Clair's.[13]

In 1998, Congress and President Bill Clinton declared Lake Champlain the sixth Great Lake through a new federal law.[14] The purpose was to make federal money available to institutions around Lake Champlain under the Sea Grant program. But the outcry from the traditional Great Lakes states led Congress to reverse course on Champlain's Great Lake designation.[15]

Some have suggested that groundwater represents the sixth Great Lake. More on that later.

In the end, it might be more accurate to say there are four Great Lakes. Michigan and Huron are actually one lake with two lobes, sharing a water level. If Huron-Michigan is considered one lake, it is the largest lake by surface area in the world. And it could be renamed Hurigan or perhaps Michuron. Or not!

There are six Great Lakes.

FAKE

TWO NATIONS

FACT OR FAKE?

Canada and the U.S. are the two nations with stewardship responsibility for the Great Lakes.

When Canada entered into the Boundary Waters Treaty of 1909 with the United States, President William Howard Taft signed for the U.S. and King Edward VII signed on behalf of Canada. "His Majesty the King of the United Kingdom of Great Britain and Ireland and of the British Dominions beyond the Seas, Emperor of India," as the treaty put it.[16] Although Canada is functionally an independent nation in almost all respects and has evolved considerably since 1909, it technically remains a constitutional monarchy, with the King as its head. Nonetheless, it is the Canadian and U.S. governments who attempt to work together to strengthen protection of the Great Lakes.

The Boundary Waters Treaty was a breakthrough in 1909. It was the first treaty committing Western nations to prevent and resolve disputes over their shared boundary waters peacefully, through a commission whose membership is evenly balanced between the nations. The International Joint Commission has responsibilities across the 4,000-mile border of the U.S. and Canada but played a special role in studying pollution of the Great Lakes in the 1960s and proposing solutions. One of its recommendations was an agreement between the U.S. and Canada to clean up the pollution hotspots in the Great Lakes.

There has been incremental progress in recognition of the heritage and rights of Tribes and First Nations in Great Lakes matters. But there is much more to be done.

Prime Minister Pierre Trudeau of Canada and President Richard Nixon of the U.S. co-signed the Great Lakes Water Quality Agreement in Ottawa on April 15, 1972, committing the two nations to "restore and maintain the chemical, physical, and biological integrity of the Waters of the Great Lakes."[17] Great Britain did not participate — and neither did scores of sovereign nations with more attachment to the Great Lakes than the King or Queen of England.

The sovereign nations are those Indigenous peoples who lived in the Great Lakes region for centuries, even millennia before Europeans arrived. Today, there are approximately 185 Tribes and First Nations in the Great Lakes watershed. But neither the Tribes nor First Nations have been invited to negotiate, sign and implement the Great Lakes Water Quality Agreement.

There has been incremental progress in recognition of the heritage and rights of Tribes and First Nations in Great Lakes matters. Indigenous participation is sought in water quality advisory roles, and in May 2019, an Indigenous citizen was appointed to the IJC for the first time. He was Henry Lickers, a Haudenosaunee citizen of the Seneca Nation, Turtle Clan. But there is much more to be done to assure all appropriate nations are seated at the table.

Canada and the U.S. are the two nations with stewardship responsibility for the Great Lakes.

THE ONLY GREAT LAKES

FACT OR FAKE?

The Great Lakes of the U.S. and Canada are the only Great Lakes on Planet Earth.

When books like this refer to "the Great Lakes," it's assumed the reader knows to what the text refers. After all, they represent the world's largest freshwater system.

It turns out that many people think of other great lakes when encountering the term. The Great Lakes of Africa — Victoria, Malawi and Tanganyika — hold approximately 27% of the world's available surface freshwater.[18] They're remarkable in ways both similar to and different from the North American Great Lakes.

» Lake Victoria is the second largest lake in the world by surface area at 26,600 square miles (68,800 square km) and is Africa's largest lake.

» Lake Tanganyika, at 12,600 square miles (32,600 square km), is the world's fifth largest lake by surface area and is considered the second-oldest lake on the planet (after Lake Baikal).

» Lake Malawi, at 1,400 square miles (29,600 square km), is the third largest lake in Africa and eighth largest in the world.

Two of the African Great Lakes are also deep. While Lake Superior is the deepest of the North American Great Lakes at 1,333 feet (406 m), Tanganyika reaches 4,823 feet (1,470 m) and Malawi is 2,316 feet (706 m). Victoria's maximum depth is 276 feet (84 m). The North American Great Lakes, however, comprise the largest freshwater lake system in the world, as they are in the same basin and the African Great Lakes are not.

Four countries border the African Great Lakes: the Democratic Republic of the Congo (D.R.C.), Burundi, Rwanda, and Uganda.[19] The lakes are within the East African Rift System, where the Earth's tectonic forces created plates by splitting apart old ones. The lakes are threatened by "unsustainable fishing, invasive species, habitat degradation, urban and industrial pollution, and sedimentation caused by deforestation and agriculture and are near some of the highest population growth rates in Africa, compounded by an increasing variability and change in climate."[20]

The flora and fauna of the African Great Lakes, not surprisingly, are distinct from those of North America's Great Lakes. Wildlife in the lakes basin includes crocodiles, elephants, hippopotami and apes. There are an estimated 1,500 cichlid fish species.[21] Savannah grasses and rainforest exist in the basin. Non-native aquatic plant species threaten the lakes.

South and west of North America's Great Lakes are Iowa's

LAKE TANGANYIKA. (NASA EARTH OBSERVATORY)

bid for greatness. Consisting primarily of three lakes near the Minnesota border, the Iowa Great Lakes are a tourist draw. They pale in size compared with the North American or African Great Lakes. Spirit Lake, Iowa's largest natural lake, has a surface area of 5,685 acres, or about 8.8 square miles (Superior is 31,700 square miles). The average depth of Spirit Lake is around 17 feet with a maximum recorded depth of 24 feet.[22] Notably, Michigan has 15 inland lakes (which all drain to the Great Lakes), that have more than 9 miles of surface area. The largest is Houghton at about 31 square miles and Torch Lake in Antrim County at 29 miles.

The Great Lakes of the U.S. and Canada are the only Great Lakes on Planet Earth.

DRINKING SEWAGE

FACT OR FAKE?

There was a time when many people in the Great Lakes watershed drank sewage.

With some highly publicized exceptions like the disastrous lead contamination of the Flint, Michigan, water supply in 2014 and the Benton Harbor, Michigan, water supply that prompted action in 2022, today's public tap water in the Great Lakes region generally meets health standards.[23] [24] To be sure that the drinking water piped to households is free of harmful microorganisms, utilities apply chlorine, sometimes changing the taste of the water.

Chlorination was not widely used until the 1920s. This would have mattered less if municipal sewage discharges had not flowed downstream toward public drinking water intakes. But they often did, and the results were disease and death. In 1918, the International Joint Commission reported on the condition of the boundary waters between the two countries with an emphasis on the connecting waters of the Great Lakes. The IJC concluded that drinking water safeguards in those areas were a disgrace.

Contamination of surface waters used for municipal systems was fatal to thousands of people. Many communities at that time drew drinking water from rivers into which upstream communities dumped untreated sewage. Typhoid and cholera outbreaks were common.[25]

The boundary waters studied by the IJC in 1918 included the St. Marys, St. Clair, Detroit and Niagara rivers. The study found that the water supply of Sault Ste. Marie, Ontario, was foul, adding, "Acute outbreaks of typhoid must always be expected from the use of such seriously polluted water."

The Niagara's problems were also dire. Although some people believed churning water below Niagara Falls dissipated sewage, "It simply mixes it more thoroughly with the water; it does not remove it or its danger. The pollution below the Falls is gross."

The St. Clair River was too polluted for drinking without extensive treatment for 34 miles south of Port Huron, Michigan, and Sarnia, Ontario. Even worse was the Detroit River. "From Fighting Island to the mouth of the river the water is grossly polluted and totally unfit as a source of water supply... Unfortunately, Wyandotte, Trenton and Amherstburg are taking their water supplies from this part of the river," the Commission concluded.

The Commission also compiled health statistics from communities relying on the waterways for drinking water, including Port Huron, St. Clair, Marine City, Algonac, Detroit, River Rouge, Ecorse, Wyandotte and Trenton. The results were striking: typhoid fever death rates were highest in cities whose community water supplies were drawn from the foulest water. In Port Huron, 33 people died from typhoid fever from January to July 1912 before chlorine was applied.

Things were barely better on the Canadian side, the Commission found. Walkerville and Windsor were in "dangerous situations" with sewage being discharged upstream of their drinking water intakes.

Those on land weren't the only victims. In 1907, a steamer traveling the Great Lakes pulled drinking water from the Detroit River, resulting in 77 cases of typhoid fever. In 1913, on three Great Lakes vessels carrying 750 people, there were 300 cases of diarrhea, 52 cases of typhoid and seven deaths.

The report helped spur governments along the border, including Detroit and downstream communities, to chlorinate drinking water supplies and save lives. But the City of Chicago had a different solution. Its drinking water came from Lake Michigan, the same place where its sewage went. To reduce death and disease, the city engineered a reversal of the Chicago River, which had flowed into Lake Michigan. In 1900, the river began flowing west toward the Illinois River and away from the lake, taking Chicago's sewage with it.

Over the decades, further advances in drinking water treatment have virtually wiped out typhoid and cholera linked to public water supplies.

There was a time when many people in the Great Lakes watershed drank sewage.

SEA MONSTER

FACT OR FAKE?

A legendary sea monster roams the waters of Lake Erie.

The Loch Ness monster has become globally famous since its story was told to a modern audience in 1933. Said to live deep in the loch (lake) in the Scottish Highlands, the monster is described as having humps and a long neck. Locals have affectionately nicknamed the beast "Nessie."

Stories of a monster in Lake Erie go back to the late 1700s. A man hunting ducks in the islands of the western end of the lake described an enormous serpent, at least five meters long, thrashing near his boat. The critter disappeared before he got a full view.[26] Occasional sightings continued into the 1980s, when Theresa Kovach, of Akron, Ohio, saw what she described as a reptilian and snake-like creature with big flippers. The alleged serpent won the nickname "Bessie."

"And you think you're endangered?"

20

Indigenous connections to a Great Lakes serpent reach far back in time. In Iroquois legend, a horned serpent known as Oniare has lurked in the Great Lakes, capsizing canoes and eating people. In some Iroquois traditions, the creature would spare travelers who made offerings to it. In others, people could invoke the Hinon, the god of thunder, for protection.

Scientists have found no trace of Bessie, but they have spent considerable effort on another serpent. The Lake Erie watersnake, a subspecies of the northern watersnake, is found only in western Lake Erie, from its islands to the U.S. and Canadian shores. The snake can live up to 12 years in the wild. Annual reproduction by females is common. Litter sizes average 23. The watersnake is uniformly gray or brown, without prominent banding patterns. It lives on rocky shorelines with limestone or dolomite shelves for sunning and shelter. The invasive round goby fish depleted much of the watersnake's traditional diet. But the watersnakes adapted and now eat round gobies. Fair is fair.

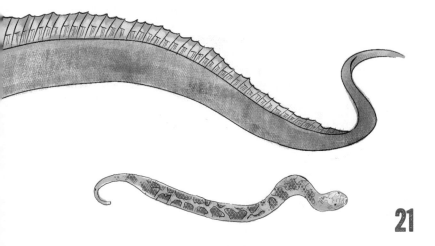

Regarded as a pest by some Erie islands residents, thousands of the non-poisonous snakes were slaughtered and the species was added to the U.S. endangered list in 1999. Extensive public education followed, including the creation of a "Respect the Snake" website.[27] Combining public outreach with habitat restoration, public and private groups and individuals helped to save the Lake Erie watersnake. It was removed from the U.S. endangered species list in 2011.[28] Its population grew from an estimated low of 2,000 adults in 1999 to 10,000 in 2017. But the watersnake remains threatened on the Canadian side of Lake Erie.[29]

Still, success of the outreach on the U.S. side shows the public can learn to appreciate and not fear Great Lakes serpents.

A legendary sea monster roams the waters of Lake Erie.

But other serpents roam in part of the lake and humans are now protecting them.

MEGAFISH

The Great Lakes harbor a fish larger than some adult men or women, a species that also outlives many human beings.

Unlike the diverse fishery of the oceans, most Great Lakes fish are of small to medium length and weight. Although anglers covet salmon, walleye and other introduced and native fish, the mystery, diversity and grandeur of the oceans exceeds the Great Lakes to many people.

With perhaps one notable exception: the lake sturgeon. The species almost didn't survive. In the 1800s, its primitive appearance (it first registered in fossil records at least 135 million years ago) and bony plates repelled early anglers.[30] It was thought to consume spawn of other species, reducing numbers of the prized whitefish. Sturgeon incidentally caught in nets were destroyed because they were thought to have no commercial value. Sometimes they were stacked in rows, dried, and burned. Some were used as fuel for boat boilers.

Then, commercial uses for the fish were discovered, including the processing of their eggs as caviar.[31] This only increased their slaughter. From an 1880 Great Lakes catch of 4.3 million pounds, sturgeon harvests fell in the next 20 years to 140,000 pounds.

The Great Lakes sturgeon population remains at roughly 1% of historical levels, resulting in the fish's designation as threatened in Canada. The U.S. Fish and Wildlife Service is under a court order to decide by 2024 whether lake sturgeon should be protected under the Endangered Species Act.[32]

The species has not recovered significantly, although signs are hopeful. The sturgeon is disadvantaged by its slow rate of breeding. Sturgeon don't spawn until they reach at least 15 years of age, and do not spawn annually after that. Sturgeon may also have been victims of long-lasting toxic chemicals. Their long lifetimes permit the species to accumulate poisons over decades. Fishing methods also jeopardized the sturgeon and other species. Dredging of ship channels removed the layered, limestone rock-rubble substrate that provided sturgeon spawning

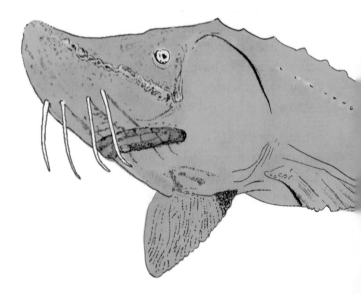

habitat by protecting fish eggs from predators and preventing the eggs from being washed downstream. Meanwhile, dams impeded many Great Lakes sturgeon from migrating upstream to spawning grounds.

Great Lakes sturgeon population remains at roughly 1% of historical levels.

Public and private agencies have cooperated to address each of these threats. For example, agencies have constructed artificial spawning reefs in both the St. Clair and Detroit rivers. Early results are positive, with eggs being detected on the reefs.

The apparent comeback of sturgeon in the Great Lakes, while gradual, is fortunate. Lake sturgeon have a unique place in the Great Lakes web of life:

»   They have long life spans. Males typically live for 55 years, and females can live between 80 and 150 years.

» They can grow very large, topping 85 inches (2.6 m) in length and weighing more than 200 pounds. In April 2021, a U.S. Fish and Wildlife Service crew caught a 240-pound sturgeon in the Detroit River. It was 6-foot-10 inches (2.09 m) long, with a girth of nearly four feet. Its age was estimated at 100 years.

» Lake sturgeon have been an important aspect of many Native American cultures. Known as nme, the fish have been a large part of many economies and a significant source of food and resources for tribes while also holding spiritual importance. In the Great Lakes region, the lake sturgeon has been of special significance to the Menominee and Anishaabeg cultures. Restoration efforts by the Anishaabeg people have been particularly successful. In 2021, the Little River Band of Ottawa Indians released 400 sturgeon into Michigan's Manistee River, the 17th year of releases by the tribe.[33]

The Great Lakes harbor a fish larger than some adult men or women, a species that also outlives many human beings.

POINT PELEE, ONTARIO. (FRIENDS OF POINT PELEE)

SOUTH TO CANADA

FACT OR FAKE?

There is a place in the Great Lakes watershed where U.S. citizens travel south to Canada and, in turn, Canadians go north to the United States.

To citizens of the U.S., Canada is the vast land to the north. To Canadians, the U.S. is the neighbor to the south. Is there a spot where Canada is south of the U.S.?

There is one place, just one, where Canadian land and water is south of the U.S. Roughly speaking, residents of Michigan from the center of Detroit northeast to Port Huron live north of Ontario.

The Great Lakes watershed also contains places, islands and mainland, which are the most southerly points in Canada. Lake Erie's Middle Island is the southernmost point of land in Canada, just 164 yards north of the water boundary of the U.S.[34] That point is farther south than downtown Chicago.

The island is part of Point Pelee National Park, the southernmost point of the Canadian mainland. The most ecologically diverse of Canada's national parks, its funnel shape attracts northbound migrating birds in the spring and southbound migrating monarch butterflies in the autumn, each species seeking the shortest route across open water.[35]

There is a place in the Great Lakes watershed where U.S. citizens travel south to Canada and, in turn, Canadians go north to the United States.

SALT AND SHARK-FREE

FACT OR FAKE?

The Great Lakes are "Unsalted and Shark-free," as a vehicle decal popular in the region proudly declares.

Some residents of the Great Lakes region, proud of their freshwater heritage, celebrate that identity with signs, personalized license plates, and decals.

One decal commanding attention declares that the Great Lakes are unsalted and shark-free, and we've already seen that whales don't inhabit their waters. No sober sightings of sharks have been confirmed, but are the Great Lakes unsalted?

Not if you consider road salt and salt from water softeners, they're not. In 2021, researchers estimated chlorides in Lake Michigan had risen from about 1–2 milligrams per liter before European settlement to more than 15 milligrams per liter. Canadian researchers found levels ranging from 1.4 milligrams in Lake Superior to 133 milligrams per liter in Lake Ontario.[36] Although these levels are well below the chloride concentrations in ocean water, about 35 grams per liter, and below the aesthetic standard for chlorides in drinking water, about 250 milligrams per liter, rising concentrations may have biological impacts.

These include killing or otherwise harming aquatic plants and invertebrates.[37]

The Lake Michigan salinity level studies found that watersheds with a greater surface area of roads, parking lots and other impervious surfaces tended to have higher chloride levels due to direct runoff into streams and lakes.[38]

Although road salt is likely the largest source of chloride pollution of the Great Lakes, livestock, fertilizer, and water softeners also contribute. Still, the simplest solution to rising chloride levels in the Great Lakes is to use less road salt, and transportation officials have sought ways to apply less salt on roads during winter while keeping roads clear and safe for motorists. The most direct way is to put salt on fewer roads. In some cases, sand or ash is used as an alternative in lower-traffic areas.[39]

As for sharks, well, there was a report of a bite taken out of a Chicago-area man by a bull shark on Jan. 1, 1955.[40] The best guess of the *Chicago Tribune* is that it was a hoax published in 1975, the year the movie *Jaws* was released.[41] So "shark-free" is accurate.

The Great Lakes are "Unsalted and Shark-free," as a vehicle decal popular in the region proudly declares.

FAKE

Only half right, the half involving sharks.

ISLANDS A-PLENTY

FACT OR FAKE?

There are more Great Lakes islands than there are grizzly bears in Alaska.

Islands have a special attraction for people. Separated from the mainland, they offer mystery, unusual history, and biological diversity distinct from or in better shape than that on the mainland.[42]

Some of Michigan's most important natural features occur principally on islands: predator-free habitat for sensitive colony-nesting waterbirds, alvar (grasslands on thin soil over limestone bedrock). Other features sometimes not found on the mainland include deer-free forests, the absence of natural predators or competitors, and unusually high populations of certain organisms (snakes on Hog Island and the Beaver Archipelago in northern Lake Michigan).[43] Waterfowl with major migration corridors crossing Michigan's islands include whistling swan, lesser snow geese, Canada geese, black ducks, canvasback, redhead, greater scaup, lesser scaup, bufflehead, and ruddy ducks. Many of the islands are considered important migratory stopovers for neotropical migrants and raptors, and harbor spawning areas for fish. Four plants found only in Michigan — pitcher's thistle, Lake Huron tansy, Houghton's goldenrod and dwarf lake iris — are found on Great Lakes islands.

Many Great Lakes islands have not always been separated from the mainland. Most islands of the lower Great Lakes were part of the mainland for approximately 8,000 years after the retreat of the last glaciers. Many of the islands in Lake Huron and Georgian Bay were also part of the mainland following the last period of glaciation.[44]

Among important facts about Great Lakes islands:

» Ontario's Manitoulin Island, which separates Lake Huron from the North Channel, has an area of 1,068 square miles (2,766 square km), making it the largest island in a freshwater lake in the world. It contains 400 inland lakes.

» Wisconsin's Apostle Islands contain not 12 but 21 islands.

» Ohio's Johnson Island in Lake Erie was the site of a prison for approximately 10,000 Confederate officers and soldiers during the American Civil War. By contrast, only 1,567 inmates were held over the history of another famous and closed U.S. island prison — Alcatraz, near San Francisco's Golden Gate Bridge.

As an aside, the biggest rock in Lake Siskiwit, an inland lake on Isle Royale in Lake Superior, is the largest rock in the largest lake on the biggest island in the largest lake in the largest freshwater ecosystem in the world.

There are 35,000 islands in the Great Lakes — the largest collection of freshwater islands in the world: 30,000 are in Lake Huron's Georgian Bay. There are an estimated 31,000 grizzly (also called brown bears) bears in Alaska.

There are more Great Lakes islands than there are grizzly bears in Alaska.

PHARMACEUTICAL FISH

FACT OR FAKE?

Some Great Lakes fish are on Prozac.

Since the introduction of Prozac in 1987, use of pharmaceutical antidepressants has gained traction in the U.S. and Canada. More than 14% of Americans 12 and older said they had taken Prozac the previous month from 2015 through 2018.[45] In Canada, about 12% consumed antidepressants in 2020.[46]

People excrete residues of antidepressants and other pharmaceuticals in their urine, but wastewater plants don't remove or treat them. That's why, in 2017, scientists from the University at Buffalo, Buffalo State and two Thai universities, researching in the Niagara River, found active ingredients and remnants of Zoloft, Celexa, Prozac and Sarafem in 10 fish species.[47]

"Fish are receiving this cocktail of drugs 24 hours a day, and we are now finding these drugs in their brains," said Dr. Diana Aga of the State University of New York at Buffalo and a co-author of the study. She called the findings "a threat to biodiversity, and we should be very concerned."

Aga's team captured for analysis smallmouth bass, largemouth bass, rock bass, white bass, white perch, walleye, bowfin, steelhead trout, and yellow perch.

Studies show some types of antidepressants alter fish behavior, including the ability of fish to capture prey.

Antidepressants, like Prozac and Zoloft, and their breakdown products were found in the brains of every fish species studied.

Studies show some types of antidepressants alter fish behavior. The antidepressants fluoxetine (Prozac) and sertraline affect the reproductive system, feeding habits, growth, and behavior of minnows. In a fish study, fluoxetine and venlafaxine led to a decrease of brain serotonin concentrations and affected the ability of the fish to capture prey.

Citalopram, detected in the Niagara River, decreases cortisol levels in rainbow trout. Because cortisol levels increase in fish when under stress, the fish can fail to respond to a threat through a lack of cortisol secretion.

Similar effects have been found in ocean fish. A study of 93 fish in southern Florida found an average of seven pharmaceuticals per bonefish and 17 pharmaceuticals in a single fish. Residues of blood pressure medications, antidepressants, prostate treatment medications, antibiotics and pain relievers also were detected.

Meth may also be a problem. A study found that traces of methamphetamine could cause addiction in fish. In lab experiments, brown trout, coveted by Great Lakes anglers, exposed to methamphetamine at concentrations like those seen just downstream of wastewater treatment plants showed signs of addiction and withdrawal. That could hinder the trout from reproducing and finding food.

Some Great Lakes fish are on Prozac.

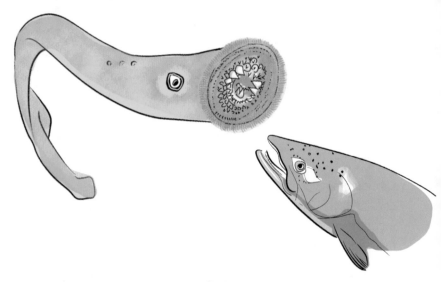

DRACULA

FACT OR FAKE?

A blood-sucking creature known as the Dracula of the Great Lakes invaded the lakes in the 1900s.

Of all the aquatic creatures in the Great Lakes watershed, one stands out for its monstrous appearance and the way in which it makes its living.

Looking like something out of a horror movie, sea lamprey have remained unchanged for more than 340 million years. Sea lamprey have a cartilaginous skeleton and a large oral disk filled with sharp horn-shaped teeth that surround a toothed tongue. The oral disk allows them to attach to, and the toothed tongue allows them to rasp a hole into the side of a host fish and feed on its blood and other body fluids.[48]

A single lamprey can kill up to 40 pounds of fish over its 12–18 month feeding period.

A scourge of the Great Lakes fishery, the lamprey is believed to have thrived in Lake Ontario but was restrained by Niagara Falls from reaching the other Great Lakes. But improvements to the Welland Canal, which bypasses the Falls, changed everything. On November 8, 1921, an Ontario commercial angler trolling in central Lake Erie noticed a lamprey much larger than the native, non-destructive lampreys that he occasionally netted. The University of Toronto identified it as a sea lamprey, and the invasive species' war on the Great Lakes fishery was on.[49]

Only one in seven Great Lakes fish that were attacked by lamprey survived. Before the lamprey invaded the four upper lakes, commercial anglers harvested about 15 million pounds of lake trout in those lakes each year. By the early 1960s, the catch had dropped to about 300,000 pounds, about 2% of the previous average.

Calling the lamprey invasion "arguably one of the worst ecological disasters in history," the Great Lakes Fishery Commission has a more positive view of the response to the invasion by Canada and the United States. The establishment of the Fishery Commission itself was part of the response, created by the two nations in 1955 to find an answer to the lamprey invasion. In a remarkable feat of research, scientists tested thousands of chemical compounds, looking for one that would primarily target lamprey, until they discovered the lampricide TFM.

In part because of the chemical treatment of sea lamprey spawning areas and the construction of low-head dams on tributary rivers that block lamprey while permitting desirable species to pass, lamprey populations are down by 90–95% from their historical highs in most areas of the Great Lakes. To maintain their success in controlling sea lamprey, the Canadian and U.S. governments spend over $20 million a year on lampricide treatments and other control measures — and will probably have to continue control efforts in perpetuity. The rule with Great Lakes invasive species is that once they're here, they're here to stay, although you can knock down some populations to manageable numbers. But the annual sea lamprey control budget is a small fraction of the $7 billion Great Lakes fishery.

A blood-sucking creature known as the Dracula of the Great Lakes invaded the lakes in the 1900s.

FACT

SUPER HYDRATION

FACT OR FAKE?

There is enough fresh water in the Great Lakes to supply every person on Earth eight cups a day for 2,023 years.

The sheer abundance of the Great Lakes may be a surprise to those unfamiliar with the region. The five lakes contain one-fifth of the available surface freshwater on Earth, 84% of North America's surface freshwater and 95% of the surface freshwater of the United States.[50]

The Great Lakes supply drinking water to about 32% of the population of Canada and 10% of the U.S. population, 28 million people in the two countries combined.[51] But if we opened their bounty as drinking water to the approximately eight billion people on Earth, how long would it last?

It's a simple math question, although it comes with many digits.

» The Great Lakes contain about 6 quadrillion gallons of water, give or take a few.

» A gallon of water equals 16 cups.

» Ideal hydration for a person is eight cups of water, in addition to water in foods.

If each person on Earth drank eight cups of water daily, individual consumption would be a gallon every two days, or 187.5 gallons annually. If 8 billion people were dipping into the supply, they'd consume about 1.5 trillion gallons yearly. At that rate, the six quadrillion gallons of water would be consumed in approximately 4,000 years. There is enough freshwater in the Great Lakes to hydrate the entire current human population of the Earth for 4 millennia, assuming the population doesn't rise or fall.

There is, however, significant risk involved in removing large quantities of water from the Great Lakes. As the Earth's single largest freshwater ecosystem, its survival will determine the survival of a much larger region. Its collapse could devastate not only vital water systems in the U.S. and Canada, but even beyond.

There is enough fresh water in the Great Lakes to supply every person on Earth eight cups a day for 2,023 years.

FAKE

— it is a huge underestimate.

"One more for the road, Gramps?"

IT'S A REBOUND

FACT OR FAKE?

The weight of the glaciers that last withdrew from the region approximately 10,000 years ago still influences Great Lakes water levels.

Although 10,000 years may sound monumental, it is a speck in the 4.5 billion years of Earth's existence. Not enough to merit a press release. But the glacial load that last weighed down the Great Lakes region 10,000 years ago is worth shouting about.

A slab of ice known as the Laurentian Ice Sheet ranging

from an estimated 2,400 feet (750 m) to more than 1.5 miles (2,500 m) deep buried the area that is now much of the Great Lakes region. An unfathomable glacial weight not only pressed the surface of the Earth down but also carved the basins of the Great Lakes themselves.

The glaciers are still influencing the Great Lakes. Their retreat has allowed the Earth's crust to recover — and it is still recovering. Known as isostatic rebound, the phenomenon can be measured in inches or centimeters per century throughout the basin. Near Sault Ste. Marie, Ontario, and Michigan the surface is rising about 1 foot (30.5 cm) every century. The rate of rebound depends on the weight of the glacier that pinned the land down. Over the past 10,000 years. Thunder Bay, Ontario, has risen about 98 feet (200 m). The Earth's crust is sinking at the southern end of Lake Michigan. The resulting tilt of the lakes to the south slowly spills water from northern to southern shores. Studies indicate that the Lake Michigan-Huron basin is easing perceptibly into Lakes Erie and Ontario, which are gaining water.[52]

The weight of the glaciers that last withdrew from the region approximately 10,000 years ago still influences Great Lakes water levels.

FACT

WHERE'S THE WATERFALL?

FACT OR FAKE?

You can't visit one of the larger waterfalls in the Great Lakes, which could have been a major tourist attraction.

When people think of waterfalls in the Great Lakes watershed, it's Niagara Falls that comes to mind. A muse to generations of artists, formerly a common honeymoon destination and a challenge to daredevils, Niagara Falls is one of the world's iconic wonders. Located in the Niagara River, which divides the state of New York from the province of Ontario, the falls has a maximum drop of 187 feet.

Falls are common in the Great Lakes, particularly in the northern and eastern portions of the watershed. There are 90 around Lake Superior alone, the tallest of which, Ontario's Kakabeka, has a 130-foot drop. Minnesota's High Falls of the Pigeon River has a 120-foot drop, Wisconsin's Big Manitou Falls has a 165-foot drop and New York State's tallest waterfall, excluding Niagara Falls, is Taughannock Falls, with a 215-foot drop.

Of Michigan's 300 waterfalls, all but one are in the Upper Peninsula. The state's waterfall crown goes to Tahquamenon Falls, with a 50-feet drop — but wait.

Another has a much bigger drop: Mackinac Falls at 100 feet.

You won't find the route to Mackinac Falls on a map or in an atlas. That's because it is submerged beneath 110 feet of water, two miles east of where the Mackinac Bridge hovers over the Straits of Mackinac.[53] These falls are now drowned beneath the Great Lakes, but 10,000 years ago, when Great Lakes water levels were significantly lower than today, a river much narrower than the Straits flowed between the two Michigan peninsulas.[54] The river spilled its waters over the falls from Lake Michigan into Lake Huron, which was also much smaller than it is today.

The 100-foot drop would put Mackinac Falls in the upper echelons of Great Lakes waterfalls. But unless you have a diving suit or submersible, you won't be able to access the geological wonder.

You can't visit one of the larger waterfalls in the Great Lakes, which could have been a major tourist attraction.

FRENCH WRECK

FACT OR FAKE?

The government of France has gone to court to take something from the Great Lakes.

A tale of the first major European shipwreck in the Great Lakes — of the first major European ship to travel the Great Lakes — has intrigued fortune hunters for more than three centuries.

In 1679, French explorer Robert de La Salle oversaw the construction of the *Griffon*, a 17th-century wooden two-masted square-rigged sailing vessel known as a *barque longue*, 30 to 50 feet long. The *Griffon* set sail with a crew of 32 from Niagara in August, sailing upstream across Lake Erie, through Lake Huron and the northern reaches of Lake Michigan, arriving at the mouth of Green Bay on September 2, 1679. Taking aboard a load of furs valued at 50,000 to 60,000 francs bartered from Indigenous peoples, the *Griffon's* now six-man crew began a return voyage two weeks later without La Salle. The crew was never heard from again.

It is unclear what happened, but the most common explanation is that the *Griffon* sank in a severe storm. There has been no lack of mystery busters trying to figure that out. State of Michigan maritime archaeologist Wayne Lusardi investigated at least 17 *Griffon* claims regarding potential sunken ships between 2002 and 2017. Only two were verified as ships and neither was the *Griffon*.[55] One hypothesis is that the ship and crew made it through the Straits of Mackinac only to be dashed up on the shores of what is now Ontario's Manitoulin Island. Some experts believe that it sank between Beaver Island and the south shore of the Upper Peninsula. A sure sign of the authenticity of the wreck would be the cannons the ship carried. None has been found at any of the sites claimed to hold the *Griffon*.

A private group, Great Lakes Exploration Group, LLC, has argued that it found what might be the *Griffon's* wreckage between Escanaba, Michigan, and the St. Martin Islands, near Wisconsin. The group wanted to be appointed its custodian. The State of Michigan claimed ownership (as it does to all shipwrecks on the submerged lands within its Great Lakes boundaries). The French government also made a claim. In 2010, the Great Lakes Exploration Group, the state of Michigan and France agreed to cooperate in an archaeological assessment. Archaeologists concluded that wreckage identified by the company was consistent with what might have characterized the *Griffon*, but that more study was needed.

As of 2023, the final resting place of the *Griffon* has yet to be identified. One claim turned out to be a tugboat wreck. New claims that it has been found persist.

The French government has gone to court to take something from the Great Lakes.

FACT

WHAT'S FOR DINNER? PLASTIC

FACT OR FAKE?

Some residents of the Great Lakes watershed may eat the equivalent of a credit card every week.

Where do plastic bottles and plastic grocery bags go to die when they're discarded?

The better question might be, do they ever die?

Worldwide studies have shown that many plastics break into small pieces, or microplastics, that persist indefinitely. They clutter the ocean — and the Great Lakes. The U.S. Geological Survey estimates there are 112,000 particles of plastic per square mile of Great Lakes water.[56] A sampling of Lake Ontario and Lake Superior fish found the "highest concentration of microplastics and other anthropogenic (synthetic) microparticles ever reported in bony fish, including 12,442 anthropogenic microparticles in 212 fish from nearshore Lake Ontario, and 3,094 in 119 fish from Lake Superior. Between 35% and 59% of the particles were microplastics.[57]

Plastic particles 5 millimeters (0.2 inch) or smaller are considered microplastics. Studies have found microplastics in the atmosphere, on land and oceans and freshwaters. They also have made their way into drinking water and foods for human consumption.[58] The impact on human

While no one knows yet the impact of microplastics on human health (or fish and wildlife), there are worrisome signals.

"Your credit card, madam."
"YUM!"

health is unknown, but they may act as stressors, entering the human digestive, respiratory and circulatory systems.

Another study estimated the global mean rate of human consumption of microplastics at between 0.1 and 5 grams per week. Variability is high and depends on the individual's home location, age, size and cultural factors. In the worst-case scenario, consumption is roughly equivalent to a credit card.

While no one knows yet the impact of microplastics on human health (or fish and wildlife) there are worrisome signals that suggest preventing human exposure to microplastics should be a priority. Finding substitutes for microplastics intentionally added to agricultural chemicals, paints, cosmetics, and detergent, for example, is critical. Scientists are piloting a system based on biodegradable silk instead.[59]

There is hope — and urgency.

Some residents of the Great Lakes watershed may eat the equivalent of a credit card every week.

DRIBBLE TO THE SEA

FACT OR FAKE?

A drop of water flowing from Lake Superior reaches the Atlantic Ocean in a little more than a year.

Lake Superior is the headwaters of the Great Lakes, the place where some drops of water (those that fall on land in the Superior watershed, or on the lake itself) begin their journey to the sea. From there, that drop travels through Lake Huron, sometimes taking a side trip through Lake Michigan first, then down the St. Clair River, through Lake St. Clair and down the Detroit River before flowing through Lake Erie, tumbling over Niagara Falls, traveling through Lake Ontario and finally cruising down the St. Lawrence River to the sea.

It's a long trip, and it takes a long time. More than a year, right?

In fact, much more than a year — more than 170 years, and that's just to flow out of Lake Superior, 1,000 miles from the sea. That links the hypothetical drop's entry to Lake Superior to when the Eighth Earl of Elgin was Governor General of Canada, acting as the administrator of land that was not yet a nation called Canada. Beginning that July, Millard Fillmore was president.

The mean time that water spends in a particular lake is called its retention time.[60] Because of differences in size, depth and current, each of the Great Lakes has its own retention time.[61]

» Lake Superior's retention time is 173 years

» Lake Michigan, 62

» Lake Huron, 21

» Erie 2.7

» Ontario, 6

And what about Lake St. Clair, that small but critical lake at the heart of the system? Its retention time is seven to ten days.[62]

Adding up the residence time of all the lakes but Michigan (much water from Superior does not enter Lake Michigan on its way to the sea), our hypothetical drop of Lake Superior water will reach the Atlantic in 202.7 years.

A drop of water flowing from Lake Superior reaches the Atlantic Ocean in a little more than a year.

FAKE

GREAT TOPPING

A condiment is named after a place in the Great Lakes watershed.

Ketchup – honey – mayonnaise – all condiments and defined as substances that add flavor to food. There is no Lake Ketchup or Mayonnaise Bay.

But there are the Thousand Islands. In fact, more than 1,800 islands lie at the headwaters of the St. Lawrence River, into which Lake Ontario flows. Why was a salad dressing named after this scenic region?

First, what are the Thousand Islands? Straddling the Canadian-U.S. border, they are a 60-mile (80-km) wide swath of granite hilltops joining the Canadian Shield of northern Ontario with the Adirondack Mountains of New York state. After the last glaciation ended about 10,000 years ago, the glaciers retreated, exposing the remnants of ancient mountains. As the Great Lakes system matured, the St. Lawrence River flooded the area on its path to the Atlantic Ocean, turning the mountains into islands.[63]

Despite the area's name, its islands number more than 1,800. To be considered an island, the feature must remain above water year-round and be sturdy enough to support at least two trees.[64] The principal islands lie between

Cape Vincent and Alexandria Bay in the United States and Kingston and Rockport in Canada. Two-thirds of the islands are in Canada.

None of this would make the area famous for a condiment had not someone concocted the recipe early in the 20th century. Not surprisingly, stories about the origins of the dressing compete. In one saga, the owner of the Waldorf Astoria Hotel in New York City, George Boldt, built an immense summer home for his wife, Louise, known as the Boldt Castle on Heart Island. While Boldt and Louise took a St. Lawrence River cruise on their yacht, their chef Oscar Tschirky fixed lunch with whatever was on hand. Tschirky improvised a dressing from mayonnaise, ketchup, pickle relish, and a hard-boiled egg. Boldt liked it so much that he put it on the menu at his famous hotel.

In another version, local Allen Benas claimed he found the recipe after buying the Thousand Islands Inn in the village of Clayton. A safe in the back of the restaurant contained a single sheet of paper. His cooks said it looked like a recipe for Thousand Island dressing.

Benas traced the recipe back to a woman named Sophia Lalonde. She made the dressing for her husband, a fishing guide, who served it to anglers at shore dinners. Actress May Irwin took a liking to the dressing, naming it after the region. Irwin shared the recipe with Boldt, who started serving it in his hotel.

A condiment is named after a place
in the Great Lakes watershed.

KING OF THE LAKES

FACT OR FAKE?

The only king in the history of the United States ruled from an island in the Great Lakes.

The United States was born out of a rebellion against monarchs. Its republican system of government, although initially giving power primarily to white males who owned property, would eventually become one in which most adult citizens could choose those to serve and represent them in offices ranging from president to mayor. In the Declaration of Independence, the assembled congress declared in reference to King George III, "A Prince whose character is thus marked by every act which may define a Tyrant, is unfit to be the ruler of a free people."

But not all Americans forswore monarchy. On July 8, 1850, James Jesse Strang was crowned king of Beaver Island in Lake Michigan, ruling hundreds of subjects.[65]

Born in upstate New York in 1813, Strang became a follower of Joseph Smith, the founder of the Mormon faith (now known as the Church of Jesus Christ of Latter-Day Saints). Smith allegedly assigned Strang to bring the faith to Wisconsin not long before Smith was murdered in 1844.

One of several rivals who claimed he was Smith's rightful successor, Strang moved to Beaver Island in northern Lake

Michigan in 1848. Hundreds of followers joined him as part of the Strangite sect.[66]

At his 1850 coronation as King James I, Strang wore a bright red robe topped by a white collar with black speckles. His crown, made of tin, was a thin circlet with a cluster of stars projecting in front. Strang also carried a wooden scepter.[67]

Strang's claim to royalty did not sit well with civil authorities. President Millard Fillmore ordered Strang investigated, and the king was arraigned on treason, counterfeiting and other charges in 1851. Strang and followers were acquitted of all charges. In addition to being crowned king, Strang was elected twice to the Michigan Legislature. He authored five bills that became law in the 1853 session.

Strang's espousal of polygamy, acceptance of African Americans and relatively liberal views on the role of women in the Church — and his autocratic rule — did not sit well with some. Disaffected church members and others shot and mortally wounded Strang on June 16, 1856. He died several weeks later in Wisconsin. In July, a mob drove approximately 2,600 followers of Strang from the island, ending the presence of the church on Beaver Island.

The only king in the history of the United States ruled from an island in the Great Lakes.

BIG BAY

FACT OR FAKE?

There is a bay in the Great Lakes system so big it would be one of the world's largest lakes on its own

Large and noteworthy bays are scattered among the Great Lakes. Green Bay, Saginaw Bay, Batchawana Bay, Keweenaw Bay, Sandusky Bay, Whitefish Bay, a Canadian and a U.S. Thunder Bay and Grand Traverse Bay are among them. Some are associated with impressive statistics and stories. Lake Michigan's Grand Traverse Bay holds nine trillion gallons of water and its East Arm reaches a depth of about 620 feet between Elk Rapids and Old Mission Peninsula; Thunder Bay, Ontario, is flanked by the Sleeping Giant; Ontario's Bay of Quinte was a transit route for U.S. Prohibition-era bootleggers.

All these bays combined, however, are dwarfed by Ontario's Georgian Bay. The bay is fringed by 1,240 miles of shoreline and contains 5,792 square miles of surface area.[68] That would make it the 24th largest lake in the world if it were separated from Lake Huron.[69]

Named after Great Britain's King George IV in 1822, the bay was a focal point of Indigenous settlement and culture reaching back thousands of years. It was a major north-south Indigenous trade route.

GEORGIAN BAY IS AT UPPER RIGHT. (NATIONAL OCEANIC AND ATMOSPHERIC ADMINISTRATION)

Georgian Bay is ringed by three Canadian national parks. It contains the Georgian Bay Mnidoo Gamii Biosphere Reserve, designated by the United Nations Education, Scientific and Cultural Organization (UNESCO). For generations it has been a key part of Canadian cottage country, a region where many Canadians from Toronto and other cities escape from the stresses of everyday life.

There is a bay in the Great Lakes system so big it would be one of the world's largest lakes on its own.

FIRE IN THE WATER

FACT OR FAKE?

The Great Lakes freeze over almost every winter.

Located at latitudes known for hearty winters, the Great Lakes each winter are fodder for photographs of lighthouses encased in ice and other images of ice volcanos, where unfrozen water leaps up through holes in otherwise total ice cover, building an ice peak. Viewing such images, people can easily envision the Great Lakes frozen from shore to shore.

But the truth is that the five Great Lakes have rarely frozen over, that ice cover varies significantly from winter to winter — and that the long-term trend of Great Lakes ice cover is downward. Many scientists attribute the trend to climate change.

Ice cover is an important feature of Great Lakes ecology, affecting fish spawning habitat and aquatic ecosystems. Greater ice cover limits lake effect snowstorms. Reduced ice cover might lengthen the shipping season, boosting commerce, but it also facilitates evaporation, which can lower lake levels and reduce the volume of cargo that vessels can carry.

Over the 50 years reliable data have been collected, the number of frozen days on all five Great Lakes has declined.

Totals have decreased at rates ranging from approximately one-fifth of a day per year in Lake Huron to almost a full day per year in Lakes Ontario and Superior. The Great Lakes are frozen for eight to 46 fewer days now than they were in the early 1970s.[70]

Two years within a decade of each other illustrate the wide variability of Great Lakes ice cover. In the winter of 2014, the Great Lakes had the highest percentage of ice cover in 41 years. But in the winter of 2023, a near-record low in ice cover enabled a freighter to depart Duluth-Superior Harbor on January 21, the latest final vessel leaving that location in 48 years.

In addition to ice cover, average lake water temperatures are an indicator of climate. Lake Superior, the coldest of the Great Lakes, is now one of the most rapidly warming large lakes on the face of the planet. It is warming up three times faster than the global average.[71]

**The Great Lakes freeze over
almost every winter.**

LONELY LIGHT

FACT OR FAKE?

The Great Lakes contain the loneliest place in North America.

Vast distances of open water characterize all of the Great Lakes. One lake rules them all. Lake Superior features a landless surface more than 150 miles long at its widest point. And Superior includes what was once a post far from land inhabited by human beings only in summer and sometimes by only one person — the Stannard Rock Lighthouse.

The loneliness of the lighthouse location stems from its reason for being – an underwater mountain that rises barely to the surface of the lake, creating a reef and major threat to the large cargo-carrying vessels that are at the heart of Great Lakes commerce.

The reef happens to manifest in a place 24 miles (39 km) from the nearest land, Manitou Island, and 44 miles (71 km) from Marquette, Michigan, making its lighthouse the farthest from land in North America.[72] Between 1883 and 1962, the lighthouse was manned, giving rise to stories about the loneliness of Stannard Rock.

Stannard Rock was a "stag station" — men only, no families. Punishing winds storms drove 30-foot waves against the tower and spray rose over 100 feet above

the lake. During high winds, keepers going outside tied themselves to the tower with rope to prevent themselves from being hurled into the water.

"From the old employment records, it is plain that many men were driven off the Rock by the extreme isolation," observed *Lake Superior Magazine.* "Marooned on a concrete and limestone pinnacle, out of sight of land, with nothing but the mocking cry of gulls and the relentless crash of the cold waves, was a situation many found unbearable. The Rock wasn't for them."

The Great Lakes contain the loneliest place in North America.

UNDERWATER HUNTING

FACT OR FAKE ?

Hunting has been done at the bottom of Lake Huron.

Between 3,000 and 7,000 years ago, Great Lakes water levels were more than 300 feet (91 m) lower than today. This exposed a land bridge known as the Alpena-Amberley Ridge between what is now Michigan's northeastern Lower Peninsula and southern Ontario. The ancient Indigenous peoples used this bridge for more than hiking.

Early in the 21st century, researchers used acoustic surveys to identify targets and then lowered remote operated vehicles (ROVs) to the areas of interest to explore further. What they found was startling — evidence of ancient caribou hunting. The discoveries ranged "from simple, small V-shaped hunting blinds to more complex features with stone drive lanes, multiple hunting blinds, and associated structures."[73] They are found about 120 feet (37m) beneath today's water level and 34.7 miles (56 km) southeast of present-day Alpena, Michigan. This is believed to be "the most complex hunting structure (from antiquity) identified to date in the Great Lakes region."

Adding to the evidence, the researchers, led by Dr. John O'Shea of the University of Michigan, found 11 chipped stone flakes with sharp edges. Seven flakes were in the southern opening of the drive lane, the rest in associated hunting blinds. Researchers speculated that tool maintenance activity occurred in the locality as hunters anticipated the arrival of caribou herds. They also inferred that cooperating groups of hunters would have been needed for the complex drive lanes.

"I've seen campfire rings with charcoal still inside them, stone tools, and even rings that were used to stake down the edges of a tent or tipi," O'Shea said.[74]

This is not the only location where there is possible evidence of ancient human activity at the bottom of the Great Lakes. In 2020, a group consisting mostly of tribal members was looking at a submerged petroleum pipeline in the Straits of Mackinac when they found stones that appeared in circular and linear patterns on the lake floor.

A rock with a mastodon-like figure at the bottom of Grand Traverse Bay has not been confirmed as associated with human activity.

Hunting has been done at the bottom of Lake Huron.

—and it may have happened at other locations now submerged by Great Lakes waters.

ABE AND ASIAN CARP

FACT OR FAKE?

A Great Lakes policy that threatens its fishery can be traced to Abraham Lincoln.

Just before the rise of the railroads, America teemed with proposals to link areas of the United States with canals. The aim was to connect farms and business with markets. Opening for business in 1825, New York's Erie Canal provided a much shorter and cheaper route for commodities to flow from the Great Lakes to the Atlantic coast. Its success spawned imitators. The Great Lakes states caught the fever.

» Completed in 1832, the Ohio and Erie Canal connected Akron to the Cuyahoga River and Lake Erie in Cleveland. Later, it connected with the Ohio River near Portsmouth.

» Not completed until 1876, Wisconsin's Portage Canal connected the Fox River and Wisconsin River at Portage, Wisconsin, but was not economically competitive with railroads at that late date.

» Michigan's Clinton–Kalamazoo Canal was abandoned after only 13 miles of a proposed 216-mile route was completed. A nationwide financial panic dried up funding for the project, whose purpose was to connect Lake St. Clair with Lake Michigan, cutting hundreds of miles off the conventional route around the Straits of Mackinac at the tip of Michigan's Lower Peninsula.

Connecting waterways for commerce made sense in the era before environmental impact statements. Environmental concerns were irrelevant to such projects. It is possible the sea lamprey reached the upper Great Lakes via the Erie Canal.[75] Meanwhile, visions of expanding commerce spurred yet another canal, and future U.S. President Abraham Lincoln was a proponent. The Illinois and Michigan Canal would provide a trade shortcut, this time hitching the Great Lakes to the Mississippi River. State Representative Lincoln and fellow legislators from Sangamon County won support for the canal as part of a political deal. In 1848, the 96-mile canal was completed. Lincoln probably traveled on the canal on more than one occasion between 1848 and 1852. During his only term in Congress, Lincoln gave a floor speech in the House of Representatives heralding the opening of the waterway.[76]

The Illinois and Michigan Canal in a sense fathered the much bigger connection of the Chicago River to the Illinois River completed in 1900.[77] The latter's primary purpose was the shunting of sewage away from the Lake Michigan drinking water intakes of the city of Chicago. But the connection also had a commercial purpose: increasing trade between the Great Lakes and Mississippi River systems. Today, the Chicago Sanitary and Ship Canal is the route by which three species of Asian carp are moving northeast

toward Lake Michigan. Although it is unclear what impact Asian carp in the Great Lakes would have, fishery biologists worry that the carp's foothold could be disastrous, as the invader fish compete with fish species for food and habitat, and carry diseases or parasites that could spread to native fishes. Asian carp grow large very quickly and native Great Lakes predators would be unlikely to control them, as they would quickly outgrow the gape (mouth) size of native species.[78]

As of 2021, state and federal governments had spent nearly $607 million to stop the fish since 2004. Projected costs were about $1.5 billion over the next 10 years.[79] Without the advocacy of Lincoln and legislative colleagues, the need to spend this money may never have materialized.

As a side note, Lincoln took at least one Great Lakes trip that resulted in rapture at the beauty of Niagara Falls and in the only U.S. patent awarded a future, current, or past president.

After seeing the falls in the autumn of 1848, Lincoln mused, "By what mysterious power is it that millions and millions are drawn from all parts of the world to gaze upon Niagara Falls! There is no mystery about the thing itself. Every effect is just such as any intelligent man, knowing the causes would anticipate, without seeing it. If the water, moving onward in a great river reaches a point where there is a perpendicular jog of a hundred feet in descent in the bottom of the river it is plain the water will have a violent and continuous plunge at that point."

On the same trip, Lincoln's passenger vessel cruised up the Detroit River. Lincoln observed the crew of a steamer that had run aground wedge empty casks and barrels under the vessel's gunwales to increase its buoyancy. This gave Lincoln an idea that he patented the next year. Lincoln's concept was to use sacks inflated by bellows carried by a grounded vessel to provide it with buoyancy. He got the patent but made no profit.[80]

Meanwhile, Lincoln's brainchild, a canal linking Lake Michigan to the Illinois River, continues to vex Great Lakes sport fishing interests.

A Great Lakes policy that threatens its fishery can be traced to Abraham Lincoln.

BTS-E 6-28-99

THE BIGGEST DIVERSION OF GREAT LAKES WATER OUT OF THE WATERSHED IS AT CHICAGO,
WHICH SINCE 1900 HAS REVERSED THE FLOW OF THE CHICAGO RIVER INTO THE
MISSISSIPPI RIVER WATERSHED. PHOTO SHOWS CONSTRUCTION OF CANAL IN 1899.

(METROPOLITAN WATER RECLAMATION DISTRICT OF GREATER CHICAGO)

WESTWARD HO!

FACT OR FAKE?

Lake Michigan may be coming to Idaho.

By airplane, the distance from the southern base of Lake Michigan at Chicago to Boise, Idaho, is more than 1,400 miles. Water is heavy — just 240 gallons weighs about 2,000 pounds — a ton. So, with distance and weight creating formidable obstacles, why would an Idaho radio commentator in 2021 suggest that borrowing and transporting Lake Michigan water would solve Idaho's drought problems?

He wasn't the only person to suggest that Great Lakes water could help solve the water scarcity in the western U.S. Proposals to tap the Great Lakes have been floating since the 1960s. These proposals include diverting some water from Lake Superior to Wyoming, draining more Great Lakes water to the Mississippi River, and building a pipeline from one of the Great Lakes to the southwestern U.S. With a drought that lasted years in the American West, these ideas and others are again making the rounds.

A new diversion (redirection from its natural course) of Great Lakes water would not be the first. There are more than half a dozen water diversions into and out of the Great Lakes. Two Canadian diversions into Lake Superior actually add water to the Great Lakes. Water is diverted out of the Great Lakes at five points in Wisconsin, at Chicago, and at Akron, Ohio.[81]

Considering all the current diversions, slightly more water is coming in than going out of the Great Lakes watershed. Existing diversions are no cause for alarm to citizens who value the Great Lakes. Rather, the fear is that increasing political power in the most drought-prone states, where population growth has been fastest, could lead to federal action to send Great Lakes water to places far away.[82]

In 2008, the eight Great Lakes states won federal approval of the Great Lakes Compact, an agreement that bans most diversions. But Congress and the President have the power to withdraw their approval.[83]

Another concern is that the Compact allows for some exports of water. While export of unpackaged water in vessels is banned, the Compact allows export of bottled water in vessels, trucks and other modes of transportation.

Lake Michigan may be coming to Idaho.

–for now.

A LAKE THAT TRAVELS

FACT OR FAKE?

Parts of Lake Michigan often end up in Kalamazoo.

There is no river that runs from Lake Michigan to Kalamazoo. In fact, the Kalamazoo River runs westerly, passing through Kalamazoo on its 178-mile journey to the big lake. So could some Lake Michigan water end up in a city 45 miles to the east?

Yes, and it could end up in northwest Indiana and northwest Michigan as well. A piece of Lake Superior could end up in the Upper Peninsula of Michigan, and a share of Lake Erie in Cleveland, Ohio, and Buffalo, New York. It's called the lake effect. The Great Lakes cause one of the greatest lake effects in the world.

Lake effect snow occurs when cold air passes over the relatively warmer waters of the lakes. That warmth and moisture rises into low levels of the atmosphere and snow falls, often in bands of intense snow that cause whiteouts and rates of two to three inches of snow per hour. These bands are often separated by sunny skies. Because the contrast between lake temperatures and cold air is greatest in early winter, that is when heavy lake effect snow is most likely.[84]

The Buffalo lake effect snowbelt is famous for its staggering snow totals. Between November 16 and 20, 2022, Orchard Park, a suburb of Buffalo, received almost 80 inches (2.03 m) of snow. The storm contributed to two deaths and forced hundreds of drivers to abandon their vehicles.

Houghton, Michigan, on the Keweenaw Peninsula that juts into Lake Superior, often experiences more than 200 inches of snow in a winter. A supersized snow stick beside U.S., 41 in Keweenaw County commemorates the area's snowiest season, 1978–79, when 32.5 feet (9 m) of snow fell. Southwestern Ontario also receives considerable lake effect snow from the waters of Lake Huron. The heaviest lake effect snows in Ontario are often on the Bruce Peninsula, which separates Lake Huron from Georgian Bay.

A warming climate will not necessarily lessen lake effect snow. In fact, warmer air at the lower levels of the atmosphere can hold more moisture and for a time could lead to heavier lake effect snowfall. But a transition to lake effect rain in the southern Great Lakes may occur.[85]

Parts of Lake Michigan often end up in Kalamazoo.

FACT

TOILET TO TAP

FACT OR FAKE?

Our toilet bowl water is drinkable.

Drinking out of a toilet bowl is an unappetizing prospect, unless you're a dog. Designed to receive and carry our wastes away, toilet water is stigmatized.

But if the bowl is kept sanitized, its water is as safe as the water that comes out of the tap. The reason? They come from the same source. The pipes that bring water to a home or business do not differentiate between a drinking water faucet and a toilet. Each person uses 1,250 gallons (approximately 4,750 liters) of drinking water to flush the toilet, every year.

This reality troubles many eco-thinkers, who consider it nonsensical to use water treated to drinkable quality to flush human waste. One of their solutions is to use graywater, the drainage from an adjoining sink. This requires replumbing.

Other solutions have been proposed. Research by a team of Drexel University environmental engineers showed that it rains enough in Philadelphia, New York, Seattle and Chicago that if homeowners could collect and store the rain falling on their roofs, they could flush their toilets often without having to use a drop of municipal water.

Rainwater harvesting is increasingly popular with urban planners and water managers over the past couple decades and is used in California.[86]

Instead of using drinking water in toilets, some utilities use toilet water at the tap. "Toilet to tap" technologies can filter out waste, pathogens, odors, and other pollutants. The process takes three steps — microfiltration, reverse osmosis and ultraviolet disinfection. At an Orange County, California treatment plant, sewage water becomes drinking water meeting safety standards within a little more than an hour.[87]

Toilets use nearly 30 percent of an average home's indoor water consumption. Older toilets use as much as six gallons per flush, but technology advances have led to flushes of as little as 1.28 gallons.[88] As water scarcity looms across the western U.S. and Canada, economizing on water — and reusing it — will be critical. There is no water to waste from the more than 20 million toilets in the Great Lakes watershed, either. Each drop serves an ecological purpose.

Our toilet bowl water is drinkable.

SWEETWATER DELTA

FACT OR FAKE?

The mouth of the Mississippi River contains the largest delta in the U.S., but the Great Lakes have the largest delta in North America.

Deltas are a triangle-shaped mix of wetlands and river channels that form as rivers dump their water and sediment into another body of water, such as an ocean, lake, or another river. The most famous and largest example in the U.S. is the Mississippi River where it reaches the Gulf of Mexico after passing through Louisiana. Draining two-thirds of the U.S., the river picks up an enormous quantity of sediment on the way — an average of 436,000 tons per day.

Much of this sediment builds up land as it reaches the Gulf. The land created by the sediment has protected mainland coasts from the worst hurricane storm surges.[89] But the Mississippi River delta, which once covered 7,000 square miles, is shrinking. Levees, upriver dams and other human intervention, including climate change, have reduced the delta and coastal Louisiana by 2000 square miles since the 1930s. Rising sea levels linked to climate change are a factor in the delta's erosion, too.[90]

While the Mississippi delta is the largest in the United

States, the Great Lakes also have the largest delta in North America — of a different kind. The 100-square mile St. Clair River delta is the largest North American delta entering a freshwater lake.[91]

The Mississippi River delta, which once covered 7,000 square miles, is shrinking. Levees, upriver dams and other human intervention, including climate change, have reduced the delta and coastal Louisiana by 2000 square miles since the 1930s.

Formed where the St. Clair River empties into Lake St. Clair, the delta has seven mouths of separate channels passing through marshland. The average depth of these channels is about 36 feet (11 m), draining into a lake that is only about 11 feet (3.35 m) deep.[92] The principal channels, known as the North, Middle and South Channels, average 1,500 feet in width.

Important habitat for fish and waterfowl, the delta was formed about 6,000 years ago and became a home bountiful with food for Indigenous peoples. One of its scores of islands, Walpole, remains home to the Walpole Island First Nation. The Ojibwe, Potawatomi and Odawa peoples of the Walpole Island First Nation call their home Bkejwanong, meaning "where the waters divide."[93] The reserve also includes Squirrel Island, St. Anne Island, most of Seaway Island, Bassett Island and Potawatomi Island. The population of the First Nation is about 2,000. Hunting, fishing and trapping continue as critical to their traditions and livelihoods.

(U.S. ARMY CORPS OF ENGINEERS, DETROIT DISTRICT)

Walpole Island is about 30 miles downstream of Sarnia, Ontario, where Lake Huron empties into the St. Clair River. Sarnia's so-called "Chemical Valley" has industrial complexes including an oil refinery and chemical manufacturer. Walpole Island's people and environment have been adversely affected. In the 1970s, two factories released more than 300 tons of toxic mercury to the river, briefly closing the Walpole Island First Nation fishery. Concerns persist about chemicals in the river and their effect on members of the First Nation.

On the U.S. side of the border, Harsens Island is the only island in the delta that can be reached by car ferry and is the only one with roads. It includes an unincorporated community, Sans Souci. All other U.S. islands in the delta can be reached only by boat.

The delta on the U.S. side is known as the St. Clair Flats, a wetland of 25,000 acres of vegetation which make up critical habitats for breeding, migrating, and wintering waterfowl.

The mouth of the Mississippi River contains the largest delta in the U.S., but the Great Lakes have the largest delta in North America.

FACT

—in the category of delta that drains into a freshwater lake.

LONG HAUL

If you traced the shores of the Great Lakes, the distance would be about the same as from Detroit to Mexico City.

Five of the world's largest lakes create an immense span of shoreline. Snaking, jutting and extending, the coastal frontier of the Great Lakes inspires varying calculations of length. All are mammoth.

Including islands, the shorelines of the Great Lakes are:

- » Superior, 2,726 miles (4385 km)

- » Michigan, 1,638 miles (2633 km)

- » Huron, 3,827 miles (6157 km)

- » Erie, 871 miles (1402 km)

- » Ontario, 712 miles (1,146 km)[94]

The length of U.S. Great Lakes shoreline, 4,530 miles (7,290 km), is greater than the Atlantic shoreline of the 14 East Coast states, 2,165 miles (3,480 km) or the 1,293 miles (2,080 km) of shoreline on the Pacific coast of Washington, Oregon and California. Canada's Great Lakes shoreline spans 4,726 miles (7,605 km).

But is it possible — or legal — to walk the shoreline of the Great Lakes? Waterfront property owners often attempt to block passersby on the fringe of the Great Lakes, although the public trust doctrine, a centuries-old tenet of common law, protects public access on the water side of the ordinary high-water mark. In 2014, University of Vermont Law School attorney Melissa Scanlan proposed "a blueprint to establish a Great Lakes Trail on the shores of the Great Lakes. The Trail would knit together 10,000 miles of coastline and provide the longest marked walking trail in the world. It would demarcate an existing, yet largely unrecognized, public trust easement and engage the public with their common heritage in the lakeshore. The Great Lakes Trail is rooted in longstanding legal rights in the beach commons that have been forgotten and eroded over time."[95]

The distance from Detroit to Mexico City by air is 1,819 miles (2,928 km). The distance from Detroit to Sydney, Australia, is 9,481 miles (15,258 km). The total length of Great Lakes shoreline is 10,210 miles (17,017 km). You could fly between Detroit and Sydney and still need more than another 700 air miles to match the distance of your shoreline journey.[96]

If you traced the shores of the Great Lakes, the distance would be about the same as from Detroit to Mexico City.

—The distance is far greater.

INVISIBLE WATER

FACT OR FAKE?

If a kind of water we can't see disappeared
from the Great Lakes watershed, the level
of the Lakes would fall dramatically.

Six quadrillion gallons of water — where does it all come from?

Standing on the shore of one of the Great Lakes, a person can't be blamed for seeing its vastness as a result of rain, snow and runoff from land. Those are, in fact, major sources of the volume of the Great Lakes. But there's a source we can't see.

It's called groundwater, and it lies beneath, yup, the ground.

Groundwater is water underground in the cracks and spaces in soil, sand and rock. Some comes from recent snow melt. Another portion has persisted underground for decades, centuries or millennia. Groundwater is a part of the water cycle frequently overlooked because it is invisible to us, beneath our feet.

If groundwater disappeared, approximately 25% of the flow into the Great Lakes from rivers and streams would disappear with it, significantly reducing levels of the Great Lakes. It would lead to a drinking water crisis.

But not all groundwater stays underground. Although it typically moves much more slowly than rivers and streams, groundwater often flows into rivers and streams, which in turn flow to the Great Lakes. Some groundwater in coastal areas flows directly into the Great Lakes. Groundwater accounts for up to 25% of the total water inflow to the Great Lakes, via flow into tributaries.[97]

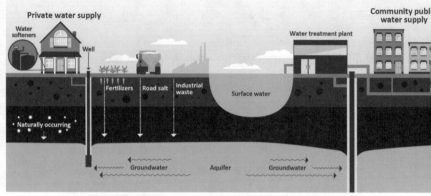

(MICHIGAN DEPARTMENT OF ENVIRONMENT, GREAT LAKES AND ENERGY)

On its way to the Great Lakes, groundwater that flows to surface water is important to cold-water fisheries, stream ecology, and wetlands. Groundwater is typically cooler than surface water in the summer, supplying cool, clean water that trout need.

If groundwater disappeared, approximately 25% of the flow into the Great Lakes from rivers and streams would disappear with it, significantly reducing levels of the Great Lakes. It would lead to a drinking water crisis.

Many people living in Great Lakes states rely on groundwater for drinking water — whether from private or municipal wells. In Ohio, 45% or 5.6 million people get their drinking water from wells; in Wisconsin, it's 69% or 4 million. In Ontario, 2.5 million people rely on groundwater as their drinking water source.[98]

Some have called groundwater "the sixth Great Lake." The volume of groundwater stored in aquifers on the U.S. side

A FLOW OF COLD, CLEAN GROUNDWATER IS ESSENTIAL TO HIGH-QUALITY TROUT FISHERIES LIKE MICHIGAN'S AU SABLE RIVER.
(MICHIGAN DEPARTMENT OF ENVIRONMENT, GREAT LAKES AND ENERGY)

of the Great Lakes Basin is 984 cubic miles (4,100 cubic km), close to the volume of Lake Huron.[99] But groundwater is not a lake.

If a kind of water we can't see disappeared from the Great Lakes watershed, the level of the Lakes would fall dramatically.

BIGGEST IN THE WORLD

FACT OR FAKE ?

Lake Superior holds more water than any other lake in the world.

Vast, cold and remote, Lake Superior is one of the most remarkable lakes in the world. While the Great Lakes contain approximately 20% of the world's surface freshwater, Lake Superior alone holds 10%.

So it holds more water than any lake on Earth, correct? No, it turns out.

Russia's Lake Baikal, far deeper than Superior, holds approximately the same amount of fresh water as all five Great Lakes. Its deepest point is 5,387 feet. Lake Superior's deepest point is 1,332 feet. But Baikal is stuffed within a rift zone, making its largest dimensions more vertical than horizontal.

Lake Superior wins the trophy to be the world's largest lake measured by surface area. With 31,700 square miles of surface, it is larger than Scotland's 30,081 square miles, Ireland's (27,097), Denmark's (16,640), Sri Lanka's (25,332), Costa Rica's (19,730), The Netherlands's (16,164), Switzerland's (15,940), Taiwan's (13,972) and Rwanda's (10,169).

Lake Superior may not hold more water than any other lake in the world, but it is still first in its class in many ways.

Lake Superior holds more water than any other lake in the world.

SALMON ARRIVAL

FACT OR FAKE?

Salmon arrived in the Great Lakes system 12,000 years ago as the glaciers retreated.

The prize fish for the Great Lakes sport angler is the salmon. Growing at maturity to an average of 15-30 pounds, the chinook salmon is renowned for its fighting ability. The Coho, which averages 8 pounds in Michigan waters, is also excellent sport and was the first Pacific salmon introduced in Michigan. Michigan fisheries chief Howard Tanner launched a program of stocking these anadromous fish native to the Pacific Northwest in 1967 and 1966, respectively.[100] In addition to reviving interest in the Great Lakes sport fishery, the salmon were introduced to feed on non-native alewives, a nuisance that often died en masse and left rotting, stinking piles on Great Lakes beaches, devastating tourism in communities that relied on summer beachgoers.

But another salmon species found in the Great Lakes reaches farther back in time — 12,000 years. Entering from the ocean, the Atlantic salmon eventually spent its entire life cycle in the freshwater of Lake Ontario and tributaries, not passing further upstream because of the natural barrier of Niagara Falls. Delectable eating, Atlantic salmon were a staple in the diet of Indigenous peoples for millennia.

The Atlantic salmon has distinguishing markers. It has a small head, blunt nose, small eyes, and a mouth that gapes back below its eye. Mature Atlantic salmon commonly weigh about 10 pounds and can reach 30 inches in length.

Beginning with the arrival of Europeans in the 1700s, overfishing and habitat destruction undermined Lake Ontario's Atlantic salmon. Dams, pollution and warming streams resulting from removing vegetation from stream sides all contributed to the demise of the Atlantic salmon in the Lake Ontario watershed. The species was extirpated from Lake Ontario by the end of the 19th century. The Nature Conservancy Canada calls the Atlantic salmon "a Great Lakes ghost."[101]

Ontario and some of the Great Lakes states are now trying, through stocking, to restore Atlantic salmon and to introduce them to the upper Great Lakes. The results are promising.

Salmon arrived in the Great Lakes system 12,000 years ago as the glaciers retreated

FACT

—although the most sought-after salmon of the Great Lakes today began with fish stocks imported from the Pacific coast in the 1960s.

WIND OFF THE WATER

FACT OR FAKE?

The open waters of the Great Lakes provide such a favorable environment for strong winds that turbines in the lakes are generating considerable wind energy.

As the U.S. and Canada search for energy alternatives to fossil fuels as part of a strategy to curb climate change, attention has turned to the potential riches of power that can be harvested from the wind. One of the most favorable environments for the generation of wind power is the open Great Lakes, where the lack of wind obstacles and a long fetch comprise a large potential wind farm.[102]

A study released by a State of Michigan task force in 2010 estimated 13,339 square miles within the state's 38,000 square miles of Great Lakes area as most favorable for offshore wind development.[103] Narrowing the total down to areas that met strict criteria, the task force identified wind resource areas in three of the four Great Lakes in Michigan's Great Lakes jurisdiction. The task force estimated a potential electric generation of between 113 and 165 million megawatt hours (MWh) to 165 million MWh — enough to power more than 10 million homes for a year in 2020.[104] Illinois, Wisconsin, Ohio and Ontario also have reviewed potential for wind energy from offshore wind turbines.

(U.S. DEPARTMENT OF ENERGY)

That's where the potential for Great Lakes offshore wind turbine development has largely halted. Strong (sometimes intense) public opposition to offshore wind turbines has restrained all but one offshore pilot development proposed in the Great Lakes. Even that one, the Icebreaker project proposal for six to eight turbines 10 miles offshore from Cleveland in Lake Erie, has met with considerable opposition. Public concerns varied from impacts of the rotating wind blades on birds and bats to aesthetic concerns about the appearance and noise of the turbines in Lake Erie.

The open waters of the Great Lakes provide such a favorable environment for strong winds that turbines in the lakes are generating considerable wind energy.

FORGOTTEN DROWNINGS

FACT OR FAKE?

Scientists have found the remains of thousands-years-old drowning victims at the bottom of the Great Lakes.

Rip currents, excessively cold waters, falls off piers and poor swimming skills have claimed many people's lives in Great Lakes waters. By one estimate, 101 drownings were recorded in the Great Lakes in 2021 and 1,139 between 2010 and mid-summer 2022.[105]

In fact, the Great Lakes have claimed lives for millennia. But it was unexpected when, in the early 2000s, scientists confirmed discovery of remains of mass tree casualties on Great Lakes bottomlands linked to events long ago. Sudden hikes in Great Lakes levels in response to climate change and rapid redirection of river channels, it appears, swiftly drowned forests in lakes Superior, Michigan and Huron. Evidence in Lake Superior includes trees that were apparently swiftly overwhelmed nearly 9,000 years ago by water released by the ancient lower Kaministiquia River near Thunder Bay, Ont.[106]

Two forests in Lake Huron, the Lexington Forest Site and the Thunder Bay Forest Site, were also drowned. Samples from the sites date the trees to about 7,000-8,000 years ago.[107]

In the summer of 1989, salvage operators in search of shipwrecks about 15 miles south-southeast of Chicago Harbor in 80-85 feet of water found a cluster of more than 50 tree stumps ranging from 1.6–4 feet with an average diameter of 6 to 12 inches, the largest 30 inches across. The wood's preservation suggested the site had been submerged since it was drowned. Radiocarbon dating of one stump showed the trees drowned about 8,000 years ago.

There are also more chilling remains — mouths — specifically drowned river mouths where rivers meet one of the Great Lakes. These features formed as the Earth's surface rebounded following glacial retreat, trapping the melting river water behind land formations at the ends of watersheds. The force of the water eventually carved channels allowing them to flow into the Great Lakes.

Scientists have found the remains of thousands-years-old drowning victims at the bottom of the Great Lakes.

HOUSEWIVES AND POLLUTION

FACT OR FAKE ?

When governments in the 1960s proposed limiting phosphorus in laundry detergents to reduce algae blooms in the Great Lakes, housewives protested because their husbands' white shirts would be unsightly with dirt, known as "ring around the collar."

By the end of the 1960s, there was near consensus in the science community that excess phosphorus was stimulating repulsive algae blooms in many areas of the Great Lakes, especially western Lake Erie. There was also agreement that the single most effective step to control algae blooms was to reduce phosphorus, a cleaning agent, in laundry detergent.

But the soap and detergent industry protested loudly, arguing that substitutes for phosphorous would cost too much — and that women, who they said washed clothes in most households, would be unhappy with the ineffective replacements. Clothes would not come clean and men who wore white shirts to work would suffer with dirty collars, they said.

Charles Bueltman, Vice President of the Soap and Detergent Association, a lobbying group, said, "if [phosphorus] detergents were banned...housewives would revolt." Dr. Richard B. Wearn of Colgate-Palmolive said effective education programs to train housewives[108] to substitute low phosphorus would be impossible to create. "We find that if you tell her (the housewife) too much, not only does she resent it, but she doesn't follow your instructions."[109]

But the so-called housewives would lead the charge to control phosphates. In Montreal, a women's group called STOP (Save Tomorrow-Oppose Pollution) rallied to the cause. In Buffalo, it was Housewives to End Pollution. And there were many more community-based groups of housewives around the Great Lakes watershed and beyond.

At a public hearing in 1970, London, Ontario, housewife Elizabeth Futer told a government panel, "I resent the implication by the detergent manufacturers that housewives are responsible for the pollution." Futer called phosphate detergents a "poison," adding that she was more concerned about securing clean water for her children and grandchildren than a bright wash.

In Michigan, the state's Supreme Court upheld a state rule requiring low-phosphorus laundry detergents in 1982. One state official described the matter as "ring around the collar versus the Great Lakes."[110]

The Michigan rule was effective. Phosphorus entering 14 major sewage plants declined 30% in 1978 and 1979 from the 1976 and 1977 levels, and phosphorus in their effluent tumbled 25%. Phosphorus discharged by the Detroit

sewage plant, a leading source of Lake Erie's enrichment, fell 40% in 1978 and 1979, with most of the decline attributed to the detergent change.

Housewives not only supported a phaseout of laundry detergents in the Great Lakes but organized and spoke out publicly in favor of it.

When governments in the 1960s proposed limiting phosphorus in laundry detergents to reduce algae blooms in the Great Lakes, housewives protested because their husbands' white shirts would be unsightly with dirt, known as "ring around the collar."

POLLUTED PIE

FACT OR FAKE?

A Great Lakes governmental agency sent several contaminated animals to England to make a pie for Queen Elizabeth II.

Sea lamprey have vexed managers of the Great Lakes fishery since their arrival in the upper four lakes beginning in the 1920s.[111] Parasites that suck blood from fish, they are lethal to the fishery unless controlled. But even effective chemical treatments and construction of barriers to lamprey breeding habitat have been unable to vanquish the species in the Great Lakes.

Three times during the more than 70-year reign of Queen Elizabeth II of England, the Great Lakes Fishery Commission sent captured lamprey across the sea to be baked into pie in honor of her 50th and 60th years on the throne and for her 90th birthday.

In the 1990s, seeking a novel way of further subduing the lamprey, the University of Minnesota Sea Grant program received funding to explore the capture and shipment of Great Lakes lamprey to Spain and Portugal, where lamprey are a delicacy. Most captured lamprey from the Great Lakes are landfilled.

Jeff Gunderson, fisheries and aquaculture coordinator for Minnesota, arranged a taste test in Duluth. Reporters, not surprisingly, flocked to the free food. Eight taste testers sampled lamprey stew and smoked lamprey. Responses were generally favorable. Another taste test with Great Lakes lamprey was organized in Porto, Portugal. The result was a 4.5 rating out of a possible 5. There seemed potential for the experiment to succeed, until it was determined that levels of toxic mercury in the lamprey exceeded health standards.[112]

But another market exists on the far side of the Atlantic, in England. By tradition, the city of Gloucester, England, shows its respect for the monarchy by presenting a lamprey pie. In the Middle Ages, nobles fancied lamprey as a delicacy. But thanks to barriers and other impediments, lamprey populations in England have plummeted. So, the English have turned to a binational Great Lakes agency.[113]

Three times during the more than 70-year reign of Queen Elizabeth II of England, the Great Lakes Fishery Commission sent captured lamprey across the sea to be baked into pie in honor of her 50th and 60th years on the throne and for her 90th birthday. It is possible they contained unhealthy concentrations, but one meal of lamprey is unlikely to have a long-term health effect.

A Great Lakes governmental agency sent several contaminated animals to England to make a pie for Queen Elizabeth II.

.

DOWN, DOWN, DOWN

FACT OR FAKE?

Scientists predict that due to climate change, the level of the Great Lakes will fall five feet by the year 2100 and that climate refugees from the Great Lakes region will move away.

When the phenomenon of climate change caught the public's attention in the late 1980s, it was dubbed "global warming." And sure enough, the popular conception grew of a uniform heating of the world and drying of major water systems like the Great Lakes. A 1989 report prepared by the U.S. Environmental Protection Agency speculated that "higher temperatures may overwhelm any increase in precipitation and may evaporate lakes to below the lowest levels on record." But even that report had some qualifications.[114]

In fact, quite the opposite effect may be true. A 2022 study suggests water levels on four of the five Great Lakes will likely rise by the year 2050: Superior 7.5 inches (19 cm), Lake Erie 11 inches (28 cm) and lakes Michigan and Huron 17.3 inches (44 cm).[115] Increased intensity and number of storms is one reason. A warmer atmosphere can hold more moisture.

Other climate change effects in the Great Lakes are palpable, including algal blooms enhanced by warmer

temperatures. Coastal damage from storms during high water periods is also accelerating, costing taxpayers millions of dollars in relief and reconstruction expenses.[116]

Despite these impacts, the Great Lakes region is expected to attract, not drive away climate refugees in search of abundant fresh water and temperatures moderated by the Lakes. Extended hot spells, record drought and increasing wildfires are expected to plague the southwestern U.S.

Reporter Keith Schneider observed in Michigan's *Bridge Magazine:*

> *Available evidence indicates that as an end-of-century destination, the Great Lakes will be among the most ecologically attractive North American destinations. The Rhodium Group, a New York-based research consultancy, prepared a study ... which generally showed that by the end of the century the Great Lakes states are expected to be among the safest regions of the country. Access to fresh water and moderate temperatures are key ingredients.*[117]

Scientists predict that due to climate change, the level of the Great Lakes will fall five feet by the year 2100 and that climate refugees from the Great Lakes region will move away.

FAKE

HURON HURRICANE

FACT OR FAKE?

A hurricane once struck the Great Lakes.

Almost a thousand miles separate the Great Lakes from the hurricane highways in the Gulf of Mexico and off the coast of the southeastern U.S. But remnants of hurricanes do occasionally migrate into the Great Lakes, dumping heavy rain.

Has a hurricane ever originated in the Great Lakes region itself? Depends on how you define "hurricane."[118] But there once was a storm called the "Lake Huroncane." The U.S. National Weather Service said it had "uncanny likenesses" to a hurricane. Developing in prime hurricane season, late summer, the September 1996 storm had an eye, a warm core, rain bands and gusting winds.

The storm then deepened and intensified at lower levels of the atmosphere compared to aloft, typical of a warm-core low. It is believed that the warm waters of Lake Huron and associated low level instability over the lake were, to a large extent, the major contributing factors in the storm's evolution. The storm then formed a broad cyclonic circulation, including the "spiral bands and eye," typically seen in hurricanes. At one point, the cyclone produced tropical storm force winds (39 – 73 mph) and some of the spiral bands even had rainfall exceeding 10 cm (more than four inches), causing some flooding.

A November 1913 Great Lakes storm, although also not a conventional hurricane, was dubbed the "White Hurricane," the Frozen Fury and the Big Blow. Raging from November 16 to 20, the monster tempest resulted from the collision of two storms. With winds peaking at 90 miles per hour (144 km/h), the storm generated 35-foot waves and blinding snow and caused a dozen shipwrecks that took over 250 lives. Lake Huron shipping was hardest hit, with a loss of 187 lives and eight vessels.

A hurricane once struck the Great Lakes.

TRAIL SWIMMING

FACT OR FAKE?

One Great Lakes trail requires a diving suit.

The Great Lakes region is crisscrossed with trails for hiking, horseback riding, bicycling, off-road vehicle use and canoeing. One-third of the 4,800-mile North Country National Scenic Trail in the U.S. winds through six Great Lakes states. Ontario's Bruce Trail, 560 miles (900 km) long, follows the Niagara Escarpment from Niagara Falls to the spectacular scenery at the tip of the Bruce Peninsula.[119] Wisconsin's waters host 400 miles of the Lake Superior Water Trail, a pathway for canoes, kayaks and more. In Ontario, the Lake Superior Water Trail extends 600 miles (about 1,000 km) along the north shore of the lake. The Great Lakes Waterfront Trail connects 155 communities and First Nations along the Canadian shores of the Great Lakes region.[120] A new binational bicycle pathway is planned for the Gordie Howe International Bridge spanning the Detroit River and linking the cities of Detroit and Windsor.

There is another category of Great Lakes trails. It's underwater. One example is Michigan's Alger Underwater Preserve in Lake Superior.[121] One of 13 state underwater preserves covering 7,200 square miles of bottomlands in Michigan's Great Lakes waters, it contains seven major shipwreck dives, and an underwater trail with interpretive signs associated with the shipwreck Murray Bay, a 145-foot schooner that sank in October 1870 in 12-30 feet of water. The underwater trail's signs explain the shipwreck and fish and other aquatic life. "Divers can expect to have close encounters with schools of rock bass and other colorful game fish," the State of Michigan says.

Although they don't have formally designated trails, there are many state and federal underwater parks in the Great Lakes. The Thunder Bay National Marine Sanctuary in Michigan's Lake Huron waters contains over 80 shipwrecks, most of which can be reached by snorkeling or diving.[122] Fathom Five National Marine Park, in Ontario's Lake Huron waters, contains more than 20 shipwrecks as well as interesting underwater geologic features.[123] It's estimated that there are more than 6,000 shipwrecks in the Great Lakes.[124]

One Great Lakes trail requires a diving suit.

AFTERWORD

Learning about the Great Lakes is fun. Working to protect them is both challenging and immensely rewarding.

These lakes are unparalleled in the world and so are the threats facing them. Climate change is the overarching danger, but there are also concerns about toxic substances, invasive species, loss of habitat, and many other problems. Now that you've read about this incomparable freshwater ecosystem, I encourage you to learn even more about them and to join the many people who are working to protect them for future generations.

I once hosted visitors from Europe who had never seen the Great Lakes. As we neared Lake Michigan at Sleeping Bear Dunes, my pride grew. I was sure Lake Michigan would impress them. As members of the group exited the van at a majestic overlook, they exclaimed over the view. "Why do you call these lakes?" one asked. "You can't see the other side." One member of the group marveled at the big lake for another reason. "They're so clean!" she said in wonder. "At home we hear the Great Lakes are poisoned and ugly.

It looks like you could swim in them." I assured her that many people do just that, safely. Despite their problems, the Great Lakes are better off in some ways than they were 50 years ago. That is a blessing, achieved by the work of healing undertaken by previous generations.

So let's take pride in these lakes, which belong to all of us. Enjoy them — and protect them.

Dave Dempsey

ENDNOTES

1 A watershed is an area of land that drains all the streams and rainfall to a common outlet. Watersheds can be as small as a footprint or large enough to encompass all the land that drains water into rivers that drain into the Great Lakes. Source: U.S. Geological Survey.

2 "Available" means water that is not captured in ice caps, glaciers and permanent snow. "Surface water" excludes groundwater.

3 National Ocean Service, National Oceanic and Atmospheric Administration, Tides and Water Levels: NOAA's National Ocean Service Education, https://oceanservice.noaa.gov/education/tutorial_tides/welcome.html, accessed February 25, 2023.

4 Novascotia.com, 8 Ways to Experience the Bay of Fundy, https://www.novascotia.com/trip-ideas/stories/8-ways-experience-bay-fundy#:~:text=Tidal%20changes%20on%20the%20Bay,16.3%20metres%20(53.5%20feet). Accessed February 25, 2023.

5 National Ocean Service, National Oceanic and Atmospheric Administration, Do the Great Lakes Have Tides? https://oceanservice.noaa.gov/facts/gltides.html, accessed February 25, 2023.

6 *Chicago Tribune*, "The Killer Seiche of 1954," July 28, 2013, https://www.chicagotribune.com/news/ct-per-flash-seiche-0728-20130728-story.html, accessed February 26, 2023.

7 Traverse City Tourism, "Are There Really Whale Watching Cruises in Traverse City?", https://www.traversecity.com/blog/post/are-there-really-whale-watching-cruises-in-traverse-city/, accessed February 27, 2023.

8 *National Geographic*, "Krill," https://www.nationalgeographic.com/animals/invertebrates/facts/krill, accessed February 27, 2023.

9 Fisheries and Oceans Canada "Beluga whale (Delphinapterus leucas) https://species-registry.canada.ca/index-en.html#/species/102-111, accessed February 27, 2023.

10 A cubic mile is a three-dimensional cube with sides one mile in length.

11 U.S. Environmental Protection Agency, "Physical Features of the Great Lakes," https://www.epa.gov/greatlakes/physical-features-great-lakes, accessed February 27, 2023.

12 *The Water Encyclopedia*, 2nd Edition. F. van der Leeden, F.L. Troise and D.K. Todd. Lewis Publishers, USA. p. 188. (1990)

13 Lake Champlain Basin Program, About the Basin: Facts, https://www.lcbp.org/about-the-basin/facts/, accessed February 27, 2023.

14 *New York Times*, "Champlain Becomes the Sixth Great Lake," https://www.nytimes.com/1998/03/07/us/champlain-becomes-the-sixth-great-lake.html, March 7, 1998.

15 *New York Times*, "Lakes are Born Great, 5 Sniff, So Upstart is Ousted," https://www.nytimes.com/1998/03/25/us/lakes-are-born-great-5-sniff-so-upstart-is-ousted.html, March 25, 1998.

16 International Joint Commission, "The Boundary Waters Treaty of 1909," https://www.ijc.org/sites/default/files/2018-07/Boundary%20Water-ENGFR.pdf, accessed February 27, 2023.

17 International Joint Commission, "Great Lakes Water Quality Agreement with Annexes and Texts, and Terms of Reference, Between the United States of America, Signed at Ottawa, April 15, 1972," https://www.ijc.org/sites/default/files/C23.pdf, accessed February 27, 2023.

18 Global Great Lakes, "African Great Lakes," https://www.globalgreatlakes.org/agl/, accessed February 27, 2023.

19 U.S. Department of State, "About the Great Lakes Region, https://2009-2017.state.gov/s/greatlakes_drc/191417.htm, accessed February 27, 2023.

20 Great Lakes of Africa, "About the Lakes," https://www.greatlakesofafrica.org/about-the-lakes/, accessed February 27, 2023.

21 Cichlid fish include many food and game fish species.

22 Iowa Great Lakes Association, "Lake Maps, Sizes and Depths," https://iagreatlakes.com/preserving-the-lakes/great-lakes-maps/, accessed February 27, 2023.

23 The Flint and Benton Harbor crises were major emergencies. They threatened the health of two communities with a large proportion of low-income residents and people of color.

24 U.S. Environmental Protection Agency and Environment and Climate Change Canada, "State of the Great Lakes 2022," https://binational.net/2022/07/29/sogl-edgl-2022/, accessed February 27, 2023.

25 International Joint Commission, "Final Report of the International Joint Commission on the Pollution of Boundary Waters Reference, Wash-

ington-Ottawa 1913," https://archive.org/details/finalreportofintooin-terich, accessed February 27, 2023.

26 Great Lakes Guide, "Meet Bessie, the Loch Ness Monster of Lake Erie," https://greatlakes.guide/ideas/meet-bessie-the-loch-ness-monsters-ca-nadian-cousin-livin, accessed February 27, 2023.

27 Respect the Snake: Lake Erie Watersnake Recovery and Conservation, http://www.respectthesnake.com/, accessed February 27, 2023.

28 Ted Williams, The Nature Conservancy, Cool Green Science, "Recov-ery: Saving the Lake Erie Watersnake, A Lesson in Outreach, https://blog.nature.org/2017/01/23/recovery-saving-lake-erie-watersnake-lesson-out-reach-science-communication/#:~:text=In%201999%2C%20when%20the%20Lake,are%20at%20least%2010%2C000%20adults, accessed February 27. 2023.

29 OntarioNature.org, "Lake Erie Watersnake," https://ontarionature.org/programs/community-science/reptile-amphibian-atlas/lake-erie-water-snake/#:~:text=Lake%20Erie%20watersnakes%20are%20found,Erie%20watersnake%20%C2%A9%20Joe%20Crowley, accessed February 27, 2023.

30 Michigan State University, MSU Today, "Bringing Back Michigan's Lake Sturgeon," posted May 25, 2022 https://msutoday.msu.edu/news/2022/bringing-back-michigan-lake-sturgeon, accessed February 27, 2023.

31 Michigan Sea Grant, "Lake Sturgeon," https://www.michiganseagrant.org/topics/ecosystems-and-habitats/native-species-and-biodiversity/lake-sturgeon/, accessed February 27, 2023.

32 Center for Biological Diversity, "Lake Sturgeon Will Get Endangered Species Decision in 2024," September 15, 2021, https://biologicaldiversity.org/w/news/press-releases/lake-sturgeon-will-get-endangered-spe-cies-decision-in-2024-2021-09-15/, accessed February 27. 2023, and Committee on the Status of Endangered Wildlife in Canada, "COSEWIC assessment and status report on the Lake Sturgeon Acipenser fulvescens, Western Hudson Bay populations, Saskatchewan-Nelson River popula-tions, Southern Hudson Bay-James Bay populations and Great Lakes-Up-per St. Lawrence populations in Canada. Committee on the Status of Endangered Wildlife in Canada. Ottawa.2017." https://wildlife-species.canada.ca/species-risk-registry/virtual_sara/files/cosewic/sr_Lake%20Sturgeon_2017_e.pdf, accessed February 27, 2023.

33 Sierra Clark, Traverse City Record-Eagle, "Little River Band of Otta-wa Indians celebrates largest sturgeon release yet," September 12,2021 https://www.record-eagle.com/news/little-river-band-of-ottawa-indi-

ans-celebrates-largest-sturgeon-release-yet/article_b42ac638-1272-11ec-8adb-2be5aa7f556f.html, accessed February 27, 2023.

34 The northernmost point of land in the contiguous 48 United States is Minnesota's peculiar Northwest Angle. Separated from mainland Minnesota and connected by land to the Canadian provinces of Ontario and Manitoba, and over water by the Lake of the Woods, the Northwest Angle is also the only portion of the contiguous 48 states that lies above the 49th parallel.

35 Parks Canada, Point Pelee National Park, https://parks.canada.ca/pn-np/on/pelee, accessed February 27, 2023.

36 Sorichetti et al, "Chloride Trends in Ontario's Surface and Groundwaters," Journal of Great Lakes Research, ISSN: 0380-1330, Vol: 48, Issue: 2, Page: 512-525, 2022, https://www.sciencedirect.com/science/article/pii/S0380133022000314, accessed February 27, 2023.

37 Minnesota Pollution Control Agency, "Environmental Impacts of Road Salt and other De-Icing Chemicals," https://stormwater.pca.state.mn.us/index.php/Environmental_impacts_of_road_salt_and_other_de-icing_chemicals, accessed February 27, 2023.

38 Dugan et al, "Tributary Chloride Loading into Lake Michigan," Limnology and Oceangeography Letters, https://aslopubs.onlinelibrary.wiley.com/doi/full/10.1002/lol2.10228, accessed February 27, 2023.

39 Michigan State University, MSU Today, "Ask the Expert: Is Road Salt Making the Great Lakes Saltier?", https://msutoday.msu.edu/news/2022/road-salt, March 11, 2022, accessed February 27, 2023.

40 SharkAttackData.com, "Shark Attack at Chicago (Lake Michigan) in Illinois, United States of America, http://www.sharkattackdata.com/gsaf/attack/united_states_of_america/illinois/1955.00.00.c, accessed February 27, 023.

41 Kori Rumore, Chicago Tribune, "Did Shark Attack Occur in Lake Michigan? Here's What Tribune Reporters Had to Say in the 1970s, July 13, 2022, https://www.chicagotribune.com/history/ct-shark-attack-lake-michigan-20220713-fms3wv7dorbldmbf6nabkptvdy-story.html, accessed February 27, 2023.

42 Biological diversity refers to the variety of life on Earth at all its levels, from genes to ecosystems.

43 Judith D. Soule, Michigan Natural Features Inventory, "Biodiversity of Great Lakes Islands: Knowledge, Threats and Protection," https://mnfi.

anr.msu.edu/reports/MNFI-Report-1993-10.pdf, April 5, 1993, accessed February 2, 2023.

44 Henson, B.L., D.T. Kraus, M.J. McMurtry and D.N. Ewert. 2010. Islands of Life: A Biodiversity and Conservation Atlas of the Great Lakes Islands. Nature Conservancy of Canada. 154pp, https://www.conservation-gateway.org/Documents/Islands-of-Life-final-4-printers.pdf, accessed February 27, 2023.

45 Henson, B.L., D.T. Kraus, M.J. McMurtry and D.N. Ewert. 2010. *Islands of Life: A Biodiversity and Conservation Atlas of the Great Lakes Islands*. Nature Conservancy of Canada. 154pp, https://www.conservation-gateway.org/Documents/Islands-of-Life-final-4-printers.pdf, accessed February 27, 2023.

46 Statista.com, "Consumption of Antidepressants in Selected Countries in 2021," https://www.statista.com/statistics/283072/antidepressant-consumption-in-selected-countries/, accessed February 27, 2023.

47 Arnnok et al, "Selective Uptake and Bioaccumulation of Antidepressants in Fish from Effluent-Impacted Niagara River," Environ. Sci. Technol. 2017, 51, 18, 10652–10662. Publication Date: August 16, 2017 https://doi.org/10.1021/acs.est.7b02912. Accessed February 27, 2023.

48 U.S. Fish and Wildlife Service, "Sea Lamprey," https://www.fws.gov/species/sea-lamprey-petromyzon-marinus, accessed February 27, 2023.

49 Great Lakes Fishery Commission, "Great Lakes Fishery Commission Reflects on 100 years of invasive sea lampreys above Niagara Falls," news release dated November 5, 2021, http://www.glfc.org/pubs/pressrel/100%20years%20Lake%20Erie%20sea%20lamprey_FINAL.pdf, accessed February 27, 2023.

50 U.S. Fish and Wildlife Service, "Great Lakes Restoration Initiative," https://www.fws.gov/initiative/great-lakes-restoration-initiative, accessed February 27, 2023.

51 U.S. Environmental Protection Agency, "Facts and Figures About the Great Lakes," https://www.epa.gov/greatlakes/facts-and-figures-about-great-lakes, accessed February 27, 2023.

52 Keith Matheny, *Detroit Free Press*, "Great Lakes Still Impacted by Ice Age Phenomenon," March 2, 2018, https://www.freep.com/story/news/local/michigan/2018/03/02/michigan-great-lakes-ice-age/363316002/, accessed February 27, 2023.

53 MackinacIsland.org, "Have You Ever Heard of Mackinac Falls?", April

8, 2020, https://www.mackinacisland.org/blog/have-you-heard-of-mack-inac-falls/#:~:text=Mackinac%20Falls%20must%20have%20 been,even%20more%20incredible%20rock%20formation, accessed February 27, 2023.

54 en-academic.com, "Mackinac Falls," https://en-academic.com/dic.nsf/ enwiki/7300438, accessed February 27. 2023.

55 Atlas Obscura, "The White Whale for Great Lakes Shipwreck Hunters," May 30, 2017, https://www.atlasobscura.com/articles/great-lakes-ship-wreck-griffon, accessed February 28, 2023.

56 U.S. Geological Survey, "Microplastics in Our Nation's Waterways," https://labs.waterdata.usgs.gov/visualizations/microplastics/index.html, accessed February 28, 2023.

57 National Library of Medicine, Pub Med, Munno et al, "Microplastic Contamination in Great Lakes Fish," Conserv Biol2022 Feb;36(1):e13794. doi:10.1111/cobi.13794. ttps://pubmed.ncbi.nlm.nih.gov/34219282/, accessed February 28, 2023.

58 Senathirajah et al, Estimation of the mass of microplastics ingested – A pivotal first step towards human health risk assessment. Journal of Hazardous Materials. February 2021, https://www.sciencedirect.com/sci-ence/article/abs/pii/S0304389420319944#, accessed February 28, 2023.

59 Massachusetts Institute of Technology, MIT News, "Silk Offers an Alternative to Some Microplastics," July 20, 2022," https://news.mit. edu/2022/silk-alternative-microplastics-0720, accessed February 28, 2023.

60 Jessica Chudy, International Institute for Sustainable Development, "Lake Residence Time: How Fresh is Your Freshwater?", September 20, 2021, https://www.iisd.org/ela/blog/commentary/lake-residence-time-how-fresh-is-your-fresh-water/, accessed February 2023.

61 National Oceanic and Atmospheric Administration, Great Lakes Environmental Laboratory, "About Our Great Lakes: Lake-by-Lake Profiles," https://www.glerl.noaa.gov/education/ourlakes/lakes.html, accessed February 28, 2023.

2 Terry Gibb, Michigan State University Extension, "Heart of the Great Lakes," March 28, 2012, https://www.canr.msu.edu/news/heart_of_the_ great_lakes#:~:text=of%20surface%20area.-,Lake%20St.,retention%20 time%20of%20197%20years, accessed February 28, 2023.

63 Parks Canada, Thousand Islands National Park, https://parks.canada.

ca/pn-np/on/1000/nature/environnement-environment, accessed February 28, 2023.

64 Andrea Sachs, *Washington Post*, "Tales of a Thousand Islands," September 3, 2010, https://www.washingtonpost.com/wp-dyn/content/article/2010/09/03/AR2010090302768_pf.html, accessed February 28, 2023.

65 Michigan in Pictures, "Michigan's Island King: Jesse James Strang," July 8. 2020, https://michpics.wordpress.com/2020/07/08/michigans-island-king-james-jesse-strang/, accessed February 28, 2023.

66 Miles Harvey, *The King of Confidence: A Tale of Utopian Dreamers, Frontier Schemers, True Believers, False Prophets and the Murder of an American Monarch.* Boston: Little, Brown and Company. July 2020.

67 Ibid.

68 Jackie Middleton, National Geographic, "Georgian Bay," https://www.nationalgeographic.com/travel/article/georgian-bay-ontario, accessed February 28, 2003.

69 By surface area, Lake Superior is largest; Lake Huron is third; Lake Michigan is fourth; Lake Erie is 10th; Lake Ontario is 12th.

70 U.S. Environmental Protection Agency, "Climate Change Indicators – Great Lakes Ice Cover," https://www.epa.gov/climate-indicators/climate-change-indicators-great-lakes-ice-cover, accessed February 2i, 2023.

71 Kasha Patel, *Washington Post*, "Earth's lakes are warming at a feverish pace, with the Great Lakes leading the way," November 4, 2021, https://www.washingtonpost.com/weather/2021/11/04/great-lakes-fastest-warming-study/, accessed February 28, 2023.

72 Frederick Stonehouse, *Lake Superior Magazine*, Stannard Rock Lighthouse: The Loneliest Place on the Continent," June 1, 2011, https://www.lakesuperior.com/the-lake/maritime/333-stannard-rock-lighthouse-the-loneliest-place-on-the-continent/, accessed February 28, 2023.

73 Shea et al, "A 9,000 Year-Old Hunting Structure Beneath Lake Huron," April 28, 2014, https://www.pnas.org/doi/full/10.1073/pnas.1404404111, accessed February 28, 2023.

74 Brianna Randall, *Discover Magazine*, "Archaeologists Have Found Prehistoric Rock Structures Under the Great Lakes. Here's What the Stones Can Tell Us," March 23, 2021, https://www.discovermagazine.com/planet-earth/archaeologists-have-found-prehistoric-rock-structures-under-the-great-lakes, accessed February 28, 2023.

75 Kevin Bunch, International Joint Commission, "Sea Lamprey: The Greatest Invasive Control Story," June 12, 2017, https://www.ijc.org/en/sea-lamprey-greatest-invasive-control-success-story, accessed February 28, 2023.

76 Lincolnlanding.org, "Park Origins: Abraham Lincoln and Lockport," https://www.lincolnlanding.org/parkOrigins.html, accessed February 28, 2023.

77 The Illinois and Michigan Canal was abandoned in 1933.

78 Asian Carp Canada, "About Asian Caps," https://www.asiancarp.ca/asian-carps/, accessed February 28, 2023.

79 Voice of America, "Officials Struggle to Control Spread of Asian Carp in American Rivers," February 23, 2020, https://learningenglish.voanews.com/a/officials-struggle-to-control-spread-of-asian-carp-in-american-riv-ers/5288944.html#:~:text=The%20Associated%20Press%2C%20or%20AP,over%20the%20next%2010%20years., accessed February 28, 2023.

80 Library of Congress blogs, "Abraham Lincoln: Inventor," April 26, 2019, https://blogs.loc.gov/law/2019/04/abraham-lincoln-inventor/, accessed February 28, 2023.

81 Tip of the Mitt Watershed Council, "Great Lakes Water Use and Diversions," https://www.watershedcouncil.org/great-lakes-water-use-and-diversions.html, accessed February 28, 2023.

82 Elena Bruess, Circle of Blue, "Great Lakes Water Diversions Could be More Numerous," May 11, 2021, https://www.greatlakesnow.org/2021/05/great-lakes-water-diversions-future-possibilities/, accessed February 28, 2023.

83 Great Lakes-St. Lawrence River Compact Council, Great Lakes-St. Lawrence River Water Basin Water Re-sources Compact, https://www.glslcompactcouncil.org/media/nmzfv5jq/great_lakes-st_lawrence_river_basin_water_resources_compact.pdf, accessed February 28, 2033.

84 National Weather Service, "What is a Lake Effect Snow?", https://www.weather.gov/safety/winter-lake-effect-snow#:~:text=Lake%20Effect%20snow%20occurs%20when,lowest%20portion%20of%20the%20atmosphere, accessed February 28, 2023.

85 Great Lakes Regional Integrated Science and Assessment team, "Lake-Effect Snow in the Great Lakes Region," https://glisa.umich.edu/

resources-tools/climate-impacts/lake-effect-snow-in-the-great-lakes-region/, accessed February 28, 2023.

86 Drexel University, *Drexel News*, "Down the Drain: Here's Why We Should Use Rainwater to Flush Toilets," March 7, 2016, https://drexel.edu/news/archive/2016/march/rainwater-recycling, accessed February 28, 2023.

87 *National Geographic*, "From Toilet to Tap: Facility Uses Sophisticated Technology to Transform Waste Water into Clean Water," https://education.nationalgeographic.org/resource/toilettotap/, accessed February 28, 2023.

88 U.S. Environmental Protection Agency, "Residential Toilets," https://www.epa.gov/watersense/residential-toilets, accessed February 28, 2023.

89 The largest delta in the world is the Ganges River delta in the Bengal region of the Indian subcontinent, which consists of the Indian state of West Bengal and the country of Bangladesh. It has a surface area of about 41,000 square miles. The width of the delta along the coast is approximately 217 miles while the distance from the confluence of Ganges and Brahmaputra to the coast is about 155 miles. Unlike the Mississippi, it does not directly discharge into the ocean.

90 Mississippiriverdelta.org, "America Needs the Delta," https://mississippiriverdelta.org/, accessed February 20, 2023.

91 Brittanica.com, "St. Clair River, river North America," https://www.britannica.com/place/Saint-Clair-River, accessed February 28, 2023.

92 St. Clair Flats Management Plan, Prepared for the Michigan Department of Natural Resources by Ayers, Lewis, Norris, and May," February 1980, https://www.govinfo.gov/content/pkg/CZIC-qh541-5-m3-s7-1980/html/CZIC-qh541-5-m3-s7-1980.htm, accessed February 28, 2023.

93 Walpole Island First Nation, https://www.walpoleislandfirstnation.ca/, accessed February 28, 2023.

94 Great Lakes shoreline is greater than the sum of the individual lakes because it includes connecting waters like the Detroit River.

95 Melissa K. Scanlan, Blueprint for the Great Lakes Trail, 4 MICHIGAN JOURNAL OF ADMINISTRATIVE AND ENVIRONMENTAL LAW.L. 61 (2014),.https://repository.law.umich.edu/mjeal/vol4/iss1/2, accessed February 28, 2023.

96 Some have walked around at least one of the Great Lakes. Author

Loreen Niewenhuis wrote A 1,000-Mile Walk: One Woman's Trek of the Perimeter of Lake Michigan.

97 Grannemann G, Van Stempvoort D. (Eds.) 2016. Groundwater science relevant to the Great Lakes Water Quality Agreement: A status report. Prepared by the Annex 8 Subcommittee for the Great Lakes Executive Committee, Final version, May, 2016. Published (online) by Environment and Climate Change Canada and U.S. Environmental Protection Agency, https://binational.net/wp-content/uploads/2016/05/GW-Report-final-EN.pdf, accessed February 28, 2023. The report noted one study estimating groundwater's contribution to Great Lakes water ranged between 22% and 42% of the total input components but cautioned that the estimate comes with considerable uncertainty.

98 Christine Morritt, Ontario Ministry of the Environment, Conservation and Parks, "Tap Water Safety in Ontario," PowerPoint presentation, https://www.adventistontario.org/resources/departments/health/documents/2021/Tap%20Water%20Safety%20in%20Ontario_May%2029%20 2021.pdf, accessed February 28, 2023.

99 Grannemann G, Van Stempvoort D., op. cit.

100 "Anadromous" refers to fish species that migrate up rivers from the sea to spawn.

101 Jarret Ruminsky, Nature Conservancy Canada, "Atlantic Salmon: Lake Ontario's Ghost Fish," August 22, 2016, https://www.natureconservancy.ca/en/blog/archive/atlantic-salmon-lake.html#:~:text=Atlantic%20salmon%20arrived%20in%20Lake,provided%20food%20for%20Aboriginal%20peoples., accessed
February 28, 2023.

102 In this context, "fetch" means the distance traveled by wind or waves across open water.

103 Mlive.com, "Whatever Happened to Offshore Wind Energy? Five Years Since Lake Michigan Wind Turbines Proposed," February 11, 2015, https://www.mlive.com/news/muskegon/2015/02/whatever_happened_to_offshore.html, accessed Feb-ruary 28, 2023.

104 Ibid.

105 Great Lakes Surf Rescue Project, "Statistics," https://glsrp.org/statistics/, accessed February 28, 2023.

106 Boyd, M. & Teller, James & Yang, Z. & Kingsmill, L. & Shultis, C. (2010). An 8,900-year-old forest drowned by Lake Superior: Hydrological

and paleoecological implications. Journal of Paleolimnology. 47. 339-355. 10.1007/s10933-010-9461-1..

107 Michigan Archaeological Society: Thunder Bay, "The Drowned Forests of Northern Michigan," June 18, 2014, https://masthunderbay.wordpress.com/2014/06/18/the-drowned-forests-of-northern-michigan/, accessed February 28, 2023.

108 "Housewife" was the term of the time for female homemakers.

109 Annette Mary Scherber, "Clean Clothes vs. Clean Water: Consumer Activism, Gender and the Fight to Clean Up the Great Lakes, 1965-1974," master's thesis, Indiana University, https://scholarworks.iupui.edu/bitstream/handle/1805/17815/Scherber_UpdatedACCEPTED_Final_Thesis-1.pdf?sequence=1&isAllowed=y, accessed February 28, 2023.

110 "State Soap Opera: As the Lakes Turn," *Detroit News*, June 10, 1982.

111 See earlier chapter, "Dracula."

112 Marie Zhuikov, "That Time I Organized a Sea Lamprey Taste Test," University of Wisconsin Sea Grant, October 15, 2020, https://www.seagrant.wisc.edu/blog/that-time-i-organized-a-sea-lamprey-taste-test/, accessed February 8, 2023.

113 Bill Laytner, "Lamprey Pie: Michigan man prepares to ship invasive, blood-sucking fish to England for king's coronation," *USA Today*, September 12, 2022, https://www.usatoday.com/story/news/nation/2022/09/12/king-charles-iii-sea-lamprey-pie/8062382001/, accessed February 28, 2023.

114 U.S. Environmental Protection Agency, Office of Policy, Planning and Evaluation, "Report to Congress: The Potential Effects of Global Climate Change on the United States," December 1989, https://www.nrc.gov/docs/ML1434/ML14345A597.pdf, accessed February 28, 2023.

115 Natasha Blakely, Great Lakes Now, "Great Lakes Water Levels Could Increase on Average From 19 to 44 Centimeters in the Next Few Decades, Study Says," https://www.greatlakesnow.org/2022/06/great-lakes-water-levels-increase-next-few-decades/, accessed February 28, 2023.

115 The Nature Conservancy, "Climate Change and the Great Lakes: A Resilient Future is Within Reach," January 15, 2022, https://www.nature.org/en-us/about-us/where-we-work/priority-landscapes/great-lakes/stories-in-the-great-lakes/climate-change-in-the-great-lakes/#:~:text=Climate%20change%20is%20already%20taking,for%20half%20a%20million%20residents., accessed February 28, 2023.

117 Keith Schneider, "Water could make Michigan a climate refuge. Are we prepared?" *Bridge Magazine*, February 16, 2021, https://www.bridgemi.com/michigan-environment-watch/water-could-make-great-lakes-climate-refuge-are-we-prepared, accessed February 28, 2023.

118 William R. Deedler, National Weather Service, "Hurricanes in Michigan?", August 18, 2004, https://www.weather.gov/dtx/dtxcane, accessed February 28, 2023.

119 An escarpment is a cliff or steep slope separating two comparatively level or more gently sloping surfaces and resulting from erosion or faulting.

120 Waterfront Regeneration Trust, Great Lakes Waterfront Trail, https://waterfronttrail.org/the-trail/, accessed February 28, 2023.

121 Michigan Department of Environment, Great Lakes and Energy, "Michigan Underwater Preserves – Sites, Alger Underwater Preserve," https://www.michigan.gov/egle/about/organization/water-resources/shipwrecks/michigan-underwater-preserves-sites#Alger, accessed February 28, 2023.

122 National Oceanic and Atmospheric Administration, Thunder Bay National Marine Sanctuary, https://thunderbay.noaa.gov/shipwrecks/, accessed February 28, 2023.

123 Parks Canada, Fathom Five National Marine Park, https://parks.canada.ca/amnc-nmca/on/fathomfive, accessed February 28, 2023.

124 University at Buffalo, Great Lakes Essential Resources: Shipwrecks, https://research.lib.buffalo.edu/greatlakes/shipwrecks, accessed February 28, 2023.

ACKNOWLEDGEMENTS

A book is not an individual's work; it is a team project. Members of the team who carried this book forward include the folks at Mission Point Press: Heather Shaw, who managed the project, created the cartoons, and designed the book; editors Bob Campbell and Darlene Short; Kirsten Dalley Livingston, who designed the cover; and Tricia Frey for marketing. I thank them for their professionalism and courtesy. Thanks also to colleagues at (FLOW) For Love of Water who are dear friends: Liz Kirkwood, Jim Olson, Kelly Thayer, Diane Dupuis, Zach Welcker, Skip Pruss, Renee Mittlestaedt, Bob and Laura Otwell, Tom Baird and Phil Ellis.

I also want to thank family, who have stuck with me even when the sticking was not easy: my brothers Jack and Tom, and my sister-in-law Suzanne. I love you all.

Other friends I wish to thank for their excellence as human beings — kind, loyal and deeply caring: Derwin Rushing, Darlene Durrwachter Rushing, Thomas and Kathy Vance, Lisa Wyatt Knowlton and Tim Knowlton, Tom Bailey and Heidi Marshall, Joe VanderMeulen and Bronwyn Jones, and Melissa Ingells.

Special thanks to Ankita Mandelia, a fine human being and skilled environmental professional who helped hatch the idea for this book.

ABOUT THE AUTHOR

Dave Dempsey has authored a dozen books on topics ranging from Great Lakes protection to Michigan literature. Two of his books, a history of Michigan conservation and a biography of Governor William Milliken, have been named Michigan Notable Books. Dave has been working on environmental issues since 1982, when he joined the Michigan Environmental Council. He has also served as an environmental advisor to former Michigan governor James Blanchard, as a member of the Great Lakes Fishery Commission and as a policy advisor for the International Joint Commission. He is currently senior policy advisor for FLOW (For the Love of Water) a Traverse City-based law and policy center dedicated to protection of fresh water through use of the public trust doctrine. Dave was born in Detroit and has degrees from Western Michigan University and Michigan State University.

HEATHER LEE SHAW is the author of eight books, including the regional guide *Inside Upnorth*, novel *Smallfish Clover*, a book about dogs titled *Born In Trust*, and children's book *The Fisherman and His Wife*. A book designer for over three decades, this is her first effort at illustration. Shaw is a partner at Mission Point Press.

ABOUT FLOW

(FORLOVEOFWATER.ORG)

FLOW's mission is to ensure the waters of the Great Lakes Basin are healthy, public, and protected for all. The public trust doctrine holds that certain natural resources like navigable waters are preserved in perpetuity for the benefit of the public to use and enjoy. Under the public trust, the waters of the Great Lakes Basin can never be controlled by or transferred to private interests for private purposes or gain. Our rights to use the water of the Great Lakes Basin cannot be alienated or subordinated by our governments to special private interests. Founded in 2011 by pioneering environmental leader and attorney Jim Olson, FLOW is tackling, among other threats, the antiquated Line 5 petroleum pipeline through the Straits of Mackinac, the commercialization of water, and raw sewage contaminating groundwater and surface water.

MORE GREAT LAKES FACTS

Distance of shipping route from Duluth, Minnesota to Montreal, Quebec: **1339 miles** (2155 kilometers)

Deepest point in the Great Lakes:
1,332 feet (406 meters), **Lake Superior**

Great Lakes shoreline by state and province:

Illinois // **63 miles** (101.3 km)

Indiana // **45 miles** (724 km)

Michigan // **3,288 miles** (5291.5 km)

Minnesota // **189 miles** (304.2 km)

New York // **473 miles** (761.2 km)

Ohio // **312 miles** (502 km)

Ontario // **5,127 miles** (8251.1 km)

Pennsylvania // **51 miles** (82.1 km)

Wisconsin // **820 miles** (1319.6 km)

Rank of Great Lakes
Among World's Lakes by Surface Area

#1 Superior

#3 Huron

#4 Michigan

#10 Erie

#14 Ontario

Land Drainage Area

Superior // 49,300 square miles (127,700 sq km)

Michigan // 5,600 miles (118,000)

Huron // 51,700 miles (134,100)

Erie // 30,140 miles (78,000)

Ontario // 24,720 miles (64,030)

Other Books

The Great Lakes are in danger of becoming privately exploited on a large scale by those who have priorities other than stewardship.

In *Great Lakes for Sale*, Dave Dempsey offers surprising, even controversial, ideas on how to prevent the fulfillment of this nightmare scenario.

by Dave Dempsey

"Gentle, profound. In *Half Wild*, we walk with Dave Dempsey and his beloved canine kin, through their joys exploring mysterious lands and waters of the Great Lakes, and through decades of environmental challenges and advocacy. This volume by one of our most acclaimed Great Lakes advocates interweaves the lessons of history with deeper lessons of the heart."

LYNNE HEASLEY, author of *The Accidental Reef and Other Ecological Odysseys in the Great Lakes*

Made in the USA
Columbia, SC
27 December 2023

29524672R00083